Drawings from New York Collections   I

Drawings from
New York Collections
I

THE ITALIAN
RENAISSANCE

Jacob Bean, Felice Stampfle

The Metropolitan Museum of Art
The Pierpont Morgan Library

Distributed by New York Graphic Society, Greenwich, Connecticut

Exhibited at The Metropolitan Museum of Art, November 8, 1965–January 9, 1966

Foreword

THE EXHIBITION described and fully illustrated in this catalogue is the first in an extended series that will display the resources of collections of master drawings located in New York City and its environs. While the holdings of public institutions are reasonably well known, the drawings in private collections are generally less so, and we therefore hope to perform a service for both the interested public and art scholarship in our projected series of exhibitions and catalogues, which will encompass the drawings of Western European artists from the Italian Renaissance to the end of the nineteenth century.

The Metropolitan Museum of Art and The Pierpont Morgan Library possess the two major collections of drawings in the United States, and both are continuing to grow by purchases, gifts, and bequests. Because both institutions are fortunate enough to be in this position, and because both owe an incalculable debt to the vision, the standards of excellence, and the generosity of J. Pierpont Morgan and his son, J. P. Morgan, it has seemed wholly appropriate that they should join forces in presenting these exhibitions to the public. They will alternate between the two institutions, this first exhibition being held at the Metropolitan, and the second in the series, also of Italian drawings, at the Morgan Library during the winter of 1966–1967.

New York is a relative newcomer among the world's centers of master drawings collections, and even today the breadth of the city's resources owes much to the continuing activity and the discerning eye of collectors whose initial enthusiasm was nourished abroad. This catalogue and its successors will demonstrate what progress has been made in assembling here representative examples of the work of the leading draughtsmen of the past five centuries.

We cannot express too strongly our gratitude to the private collectors in our neighborhood, who have co-operated without reservation in lending their major drawings for public exhibition. As the directors of the two sponsoring museums, we are fortunate in having as curators of our drawings collections two leaders in the field, Felice Stampfle at the Morgan Library and Jacob Bean at the Metropolitan Museum. Together they have selected the exhibition and written the catalogue; we are grateful indeed for their discrimination and their scholarship.

JAMES J. RORIMER
FREDERICK B. ADAMS, JR.

Preface

THE EXTRAORDINARY variety and richness of Italian draughtsmanship in the Renaissance has stimulated collectors since the days of Vasari, who viewed it firsthand. Italian drawings of this period have always been the most sought after of European drawings of any school, and American collectors when they have acquired Italian drawings have followed the example set by their distinguished European predecessors. The present exhibition is limited to Italian Renaissance drawings in New York and its immediate vicinity; the restriction is deliberate as the exhibition is intended to point up the exceptional resources of one city.

The history of the collecting of drawings in New York goes back nearly a hundred years. In 1880, Cornelius Vanderbilt bought from the pioneering collector James Jackson Jarves and immediately presented to the Metropolitan Museum a group of 670 "old master drawings" that became the nucleus of the Museum's collection. Seven years later, in 1887, there followed a further gift of 181 drawings given by Cephas G. Thompson. Though these groups contain certain interesting drawings, the mass of the material consists of drawings of indifferent quality, many of which are copies of celebrated works, and it is significant that no drawing from either of these sources figures in the exhibition.

It was in the opening years of this century in New York that Italian drawings began to be acquired with more critical discrimination. The first significant date was 1901; it was then that the Misses Hewitt purchased from Giovanni Piancastelli in Rome a large group of drawings, which are now the heart of the collection of drawings at the Cooper Union Museum. A sketch by Francesco Salviati (No. 101 in the present exhibition) stands as a token of this group, which is particularly rich in ornamental material of the seventeenth and eighteenth centuries. The next milestone was the appointment in 1906 of the gifted English critic and connoisseur Roger Fry as Curator of Paintings at the Metropolitan Museum, shortly after purchase funds had become available through the bequest of Jacob Rogers. Fry's keen interest stimulated the Metropolitan's first purchases of drawings; the brush drawing by Amico Aspertini in the exhibition (No. 35), purchased as the work of Leonbruno, shows the sharpness of Fry's discerning eye for quality.

Linked with Fry's name in the annals of American collecting is that of the greatest New York collector of all, J. Pierpont Morgan, who as President of the Metropolitan Museum was in large part responsible for Fry's curatorial appointment. The vast range of Morgan's interests is apparent in the sumptuous treasures he left to the Morgan Library and to the Metropolitan. As a collector of drawings, Morgan's major purchase was the acquisition in 1910 of the greater part of the remarkable collection of the drawings of the English artist and *marchand amateur* Charles Fairfax Murray. This group today forms the substantial core of the constantly increasing collection of drawings at the Morgan Library. With the acquisition of the Fairfax Murray drawings New York gained its first classic collection of drawings, ranging through all the major European schools with primary emphasis on Italian draughtsmanship. The arrival of this rich and encyclopedic collection in New York was clearly a stimulus to collecting in the city. In the middle of the First World War, in 1917, the Metropolitan Museum purchased a number of drawings of the highest interest at the London sale of the collection of the Earls of Pembroke and Montgomery. In the same year two capital drawings by Leonardo were purchased by the Metropolitan in New York itself (Nos. 15, 17), and a policy of systematic purchase was launched.

It was as a private collector that Morgan had purchased the Fairfax Murray drawings, and the standards he set have been continued by several generations of private collectors in the city. Chronologically, Robert Lehman was perhaps the first of the lenders to the present exhibition to follow the lead of Pierpont Morgan, and over a period of years he has built up a rich collection of drawings in which Italian masters predominate; a number of the rarest and earliest drawings in this exhibition are his.

Somewhat later Janos Scholz began acquiring Italian drawings, and during the past thirty years he has put together a collection distinguished by its breadth and variety, encompassing as it does every major and many minor Italian schools. Walter C. Baker, first a collector of classical antiquities, turned his attention to drawings at the end of the Second World War, and in twenty years has made with great discrimination a number of significant acquisitions. In these postwar years other collectors represented in the exhibition by important loans have been active. Like Janos Scholz, many of these collectors were born or educated abroad: Curtis O. Baer, Mrs. Edward Fowles, Mrs. Richard Krautheimer, Bertina Suida Manning, the late Siegfried Schwarz, and Benjamin Sonnenberg. Ian Woodner is an active collector of drawings, while James J. Rorimer inherited those he possesses from his father, Louis Rorimer of Cleveland. Stephen Currier and John Mooney are representative of a younger generation of New York collectors.

The selection has been made with the intent to point up the range and quality of Italian drawings of the Renaissance in public and private collections in this city. The exhibition is not and could not be didactically complete. Nevertheless, it provides a remarkably full illustration of the main trends of Italian draughtsmanship from the middle of the fifteenth century through the end of the sixteenth. The preferences of New York collectors and curators, as well as the ever-diminishing availability of Italian Renaissance drawings, are both factors that give New York collections, and thus this exhibition, their particular character. One school, that of Parma, is lavishly represented, with splendid examples of the graceful draughtsmanship of Correggio, Parmigianino, and their followers. Venice is accounted for by fine examples, the representation of Paolo Veronese being especially strong. Almost every major Tuscan and Roman draughtsman is present in at least one work; Leonardo, Michelangelo, and Raphael are all here. It may seem curious that works by Raphael, one of the greatest draughtsmen of the period, are outnumbered by the drawings of his assistant, Perino del Vaga, a most talented artist but not of the stature of his master. New York's resources are here reflected: there are but three drawings by Raphael in New York, while the four fine examples of Perino in the exhibition are only a token of the considerable number of drawings by this artist in the city. The quality or the historical significance of each individual sheet has been the guiding factor in the choices made. Where New York's resources are particularly rich, this strength has been purposely emphasized.

The catalogue follows a chronological arrangement, the date of an artist's birth determining his place in the sequence, without regard to local schools. The bibliography is selective, limited to essential references. A list of works and exhibitions cited in abbreviated form precedes the catalogue notices. Only those exhibitions commemorated by a descriptive catalogue are listed.

We should like to express our gratitude to the collectors and institutions that have so generously lent to this exhibition. The frequency with which the names of A. E. Popham, Philip Pouncey, and J. A. Gere are encountered in the catalogue entries makes clear the extent of our debt to these distinguished English colleagues. Elaine Evans Dee, Assistant Curator at the Morgan Library, and Linda Boyer of the Metropolitan Museum have been of the greatest assistance in the preparation of the catalogue, as have also Georg Szabó, Curator of The Lehman Collection, and Victoria Robertson. Alexander J. Yow, Conservator at the Morgan Library, and Merritt Safford, Associate Conservator of Drawings and Prints at the Metropolitan Museum, have provided useful counsel in a number of instances. Thanks are also due to Ruth S. Kraemer and Mrs. William Truslow for their helpfulness.

JACOB BEAN,
Curator of Drawings,
The Metropolitan Museum of Art

FELICE STAMPFLE,
Curator of Drawings and Prints,
The Pierpont Morgan Library

9

Lenders to the Exhibition

Curtis O. Baer

Walter C. Baker

The Cooper Union Museum

Stephen R. Currier

Mrs. Edward Fowles

Mrs. Richard Krautheimer

Robert Lehman

Robert and Bertina Suida Manning

John Mooney

James J. Rorimer

Janos Scholz

Mrs. S. Schwarz

Benjamin Sonnenberg

Ian Woodner

Two anonymous lenders

Table of Contents

Works Cited in an Abbreviated Form

Bartsch
   Adam Bartsch, *Le Peintre graveur*, 21 vols., Vienna, 1803–1821.

Bean, *100 European Drawings*
   Jacob Bean, *100 European Drawings in The Metropolitan Museum of Art*, New York, 1964.

Berenson, 1903
   Bernard Berenson, *The Drawings of the Florentine Painters*, 2 vols., London, 1903.

Berenson, 1938
   Bernard Berenson, *The Drawings of the Florentine Painters*, amplified ed., 3 vols., Chicago, 1938.

Berenson, 1961
   Bernard Berenson, *I Disegni dei pittori fiorentini*, 3 vols., Milan, 1961.

Berenson, *Lotto*, 1955
   Bernard Berenson, *Lotto*, Milan, 1955.

Berenson, *Lotto*, 1956
   Bernard Berenson, *Lorenzo Lotto*, New York, 1956.

Bodmer, *Leonardo*
   Heinrich Bodmer, *Leonardo. Des Meisters Gemälde und Zeichnungen*, Stuttgart, 1931.

Briquet
   C. M. Briquet, *Les Filigranes. Dictionnaire historique des marques du papier*, 4 vols., Geneva, 1907.

Clark, *Leonardo*
   Kenneth Clark, *Leonardo da Vinci, an Account of his Development as an Artist*, 2nd ed., Cambridge, 1952.

Commissione Vinciana
   I Manoscritti e i disegni di Leonardo da Vinci pubblicati dalla Reale Commissione Vinciana. Disegni, Adolfo Venturi, ed., 4 vols., Rome, 1928–1936.

Fairfax Murray
   C. Fairfax Murray, *Drawings by the Old Masters, Collection of J. Pierpont Morgan*, 4 vols., London, 1905–1912.

Ferrari, *Romanino*
   Maria Luisa Ferrari, *Il Romanino*, Milan, 1961.

Fiocco, *Veronese*, 1928
   Giuseppe Fiocco, *Paolo Veronese*, Bologna, 1928.

Fiocco, *Veronese*, 1934
   Giuseppe Fiocco, *Paolo Veronese*, Rome, 1934.

Fischel
   Oskar Fischel, *Raphaels Zeichnungen*, 8 portfolios with text, Berlin, 1913–1941.

Freedberg, *Parmigianino*
   Sydney J. Freedberg, *Parmigianino. His Works in Painting*, Cambridge, Massachusetts, 1950.

Gramberg, *Düsseldorfer Skizzenbücher*
   Werner Gramberg, *Die Düsseldorfer Skizzenbücher des Guglielmo della Porta*, Berlin, 1964.

Heaton-Sessions, *Art Bulletin*, 1954
   Charlotte Heaton-Sessions, "Drawings Attributed to Correggio at the Metropolitan Museum of Art," *Art Bulletin*, XXXVI, 1954, no. 3, pp. 224–228.

Heydenreich, *Leonardo*
   Ludwig H. Heydenreich, *Leonardo da Vinci*, 2 vols., New York, 1954.

The Lawrence Gallery. Fourth Exhibition
   The Lawrence Gallery. Fourth Exhibition. A Catalogue of One Hundred Original Drawings by Il Parmigiano and Ant. A. da Coreggio, Collected by Sir Thomas Lawrence, London, 1836.

The Lawrence Gallery. Fifth Exhibition
   The Lawrence Gallery. Fifth Exhibition. A Catalogue of One Hundred Original Drawings by J. Romano, F. Primaticcio, L. da Vinci, and Pierino del Vaga, Collected by Sir Thomas Lawrence, London, 1836.

The Lawrence Gallery. Seventh Exhibition
   The Lawrence Gallery. Seventh Exhibition. A Catalogue of One Hundred Original Drawings by Zucchero, Andrea del Sarto, Polidore da Caravaggio, and Fra Bartolomeo, Collected by Sir Thomas Lawrence, London, 1836.

Lugt
   Frits Lugt, *Les Marques de collections de dessins et d'estampes . . .*, Amsterdam, 1921.

Lugt S.
   Frits Lugt, *Les Marques de collections de dessins et d'estampes . . . Supplément*, The Hague, 1956.

Van Marle, *Italian Schools of Painting*
   Raimond Van Marle, *The Development of the Italian Schools of Painting*, 19 vols., The Hague, 1923–1936.

Metropolitan Museum, *European Drawings*, I
   Metropolitan Museum of Art, *European Drawings from the Collection of The Metropolitan Museum of Art*, I, *Italian Drawings*, New York, 1942.

Metz, *Imitations of Drawings*
   C. M. Metz, *Imitations of Ancient and Modern Drawings . . .*, London, 1798.

Mongan, *One Hundred Drawings*
Agnes Mongan, ed., *One Hundred Master Drawings*, Cambridge, Massachusetts, 1949.

Morgan Library, *Third Fellows Report, 1952*, etc.
The Pierpont Morgan Library, Frederick B. Adams, Jr., compiler, *Annual Report to the Fellows of The Pierpont Morgan Library*, 1950 to date.

Moskowitz, ed., *Great Drawings*
Ira Moskowitz, ed., *Great Drawings of All Time*, 4 vols., New York, 1962.

Parker, *Ashmolean Catalogue*, II
K. T. Parker, *Catalogue of the Drawings in the Ashmolean Museum*, II, *Italian Schools*, Oxford, 1956.

Passavant, *Raphaël et son père*
J.-D. Passavant, *Raphaël d'Urbin et son père Giovanni Santi*, 2 vols., Paris, 1860.

Popham, *Correggio's Drawings*
A. E. Popham, *Correggio's Drawings*, London, 1957.

Popham, *Leonardo*
A. E. Popham, *The Drawings of Leonardo da Vinci*, 2nd ed., London, 1949.

Popham, *Parmigianino*
A. E. Popham, *The Drawings of Parmigianino*, London, 1953.

Popham–Wilde, *Italian Drawings at Windsor*
A. E. Popham and Johannes Wilde, *The Italian Drawings of the XV and XVI Centuries . . . at Windsor Castle*, London, 1949.

Popp, *Leonardo*
Anny E. Popp, *Leonardo da Vinci. Zeichnungen*, Munich, 1928.

Ricci, *Correggio*
Corrado Ricci, *Correggio*, London—New York, 1930.

Sanminiatelli, *Burlington Magazine*, 1955
Donato Sanminiatelli, "The Sketches of Domenico Beccafumi," *Burlington Magazine*, XCVII, 1955, pp. 35–40.

Strong, *Wilton House Drawings*
S. Arthur Strong, *Reproductions in Facsimile of Drawings by the Old Masters in the Collection of the Earl of Pembroke and Montgomery at Wilton House*, London, 1900.

Sturge Moore, *Correggio*
T. Sturge Moore, *Correggio*, London, 1906.

Suida, *Leonardo*
Wilhelm Suida, *Leonardo und sein Kreis*, Munich, 1929.

Thieme–Becker
Ulrich Thieme and Felix Becker, *Allgemeines Lexikon der Bildenden Künstler*, Leipzig, 1907–1947.

Tietze, *European Master Drawings*
Hans Tietze, *European Master Drawings in the United States*, New York, 1947.

Tietze, *Titian*
Hans Tietze, *Titian, the Paintings and Drawings*, London, 1950.

Tietze, *Venetian Drawings*
Hans Tietze and E. Tietze-Conrat, *The Drawings of the Venetian Painters in the 15th and 16th Centuries*, New York, 1944.

Vasari Society
The Vasari Society for the Reproduction of Drawings by Old Masters, first series, 10 parts, London, 1905–1915; second series, 16 parts, London, 1920–1935.

Venturi
Adolfo Venturi, *Storia dell' arte italiana*, 11 vols., Milan, 1901–1939.

Virch, *Baker Collection*
Claus Virch, *Master Drawings in the Collection of Walter C. Baker*, New York, 1962 (privately printed).

Vivant-Denon, *Monuments*
Monuments des arts du dessin chez les peuples tant anciens que modernes, recueillis par le baron Vivant Denon . . . , décrits et expliqués par Amaury Duval, 4 vols., Paris, 1829.

Wickhoff, *Albertina*
Franz Wickhoff, "Die italienischen Handzeichnungen der Albertina. II Theil. Die römische Schule," *Jahrbuch der Kunsthistorischen Sammlungen des Allerhöchsten Kaiserhauses*, XIII, 1892, pp. CLXXV–CCLXXXIII.

Fra Filippo Lippi (?)

Florence about 1406–Spoleto 1469

1 St. Matthew in His Study

Pen and brown ink, brown wash on paper tinted pink. 4⅜ × 4⁷⁄₁₆ inches (11.1 × 11.3 cm.). Lined.

Inscribed in pen and brown ink at lower left, *Raphael Urbino*; at lower center, *Corregio*. Inscribed on verso with Richardson numbers.

Incorrectly described as an Annunciation when it was sold at Stuttgart in 1949, the drawing shows the Evangelist, scroll or book in hand, seated in the compact enclosure of his cell, his head lowered deferentially as he listens to the angel or winged man who points out a passage in another book resting on a stand. The saint is strikingly close in pose, facial type, and mood to figures in Fra Filippo's paintings. One assumes that there must have been three additional roundels devoted to the other Evangelists and executed with a similar refined delicacy.

PROVENANCE: Jonathan Richardson Senior (Lugt 2183); Prince Johann Georg of Saxony (Lugt S. 1162c); sale no. 6, Stuttgart, Kunstkabinett, October 26–28, 1949, no. 1022; Walter Hugelshofer.

Private Collection

Francesco di Stefano, called Pesellino

Florence about 1422–Florence 1457

2 St. Philip Seated, Holding Book and Cross

Brush and brown wash, heightened with white, over black chalk. 10¾ × 7½ inches (27.3 × 19 cm.). Watermark: Briquet 6062.

This study of a seated Apostle was very recently identified as the work of Pesellino by W. R. Jeudwine, who pointed out its close correspondence with a drawing in the Uffizi of similar technique representing a seated draped youth, convincingly given to Pesellino by Berenson (repr. Berenson, 1938, no. 1838 B, fig. 186). The elaborate modeling in brush and brown wash, the Northern complexity of the drapery folds, the drawing of the broad, rather flat hands and feet, even the facial types, are strikingly similar in both drawings. All the stylistic characteristics that distinguish these two drawings can be recognized in Pesellino's only documented work, the altarpiece representing the *Trinity with Four Male Saints* now in the National Gallery in London, a work left unfinished at the artist's death in 1457 and completed in Fra Filippo Lippi's studio (repr. Bernard Berenson, *Italian Pictures of the Renaissance. Florentine School*, II, London, 1963, pl. 833).

PROVENANCE: Victor Bloch, London; Bloch sale, London, Sotheby's, Part 3, November 12, 1964, no. 4 (as Florentine school, fifteenth century); purchased by the Metropolitan Museum in London, 1965.

EXHIBITIONS: London, W. R. Jeudwine, at Alpine Club Gallery, "Exhibition of Old Master Drawings," 1965, no. 3, pl. 1.

The Metropolitan Museum of Art Rogers Fund, 65.112.1

Giovanni Bellini

Venice about 1431–Venice 1516

3 Christ's Descent into Limbo

Pen and brown ink. 10⅝ × 7⅞ inches (27 × 20 cm.).

This is one of a group of more or less related drawings which have been alternately attributed to Mantegna and Giovanni Bellini for several generations. The growing body of evidence is now generally thought to point to Giovanni Bellini although, as the latest critic to pronounce on the Lehman drawing, Heinemann rejects the "Bellini (?)" ascription put forth by Byam Shaw and endorsed by Popham, and speaks once more of the "orbita di Andrea Mantegna."

Byam Shaw's succinct summary of the involved problem of the *Descent into Limbo* and the related material, made at the time of the Royal Academy exhibition in 1953, still stands: "This is a variant of two Mantegnesque compositions, known from various sources: (1) two engravings of Mantegna's immediate school, probably from a drawing by the master (A. M. Hind, *Corpus of Early Italian Engravings*, 500, 501); (2) a picture by Giovanni Bellini in the Bristol Gallery, based on one of the engravings referred to; (3) a drawing in the École des Beaux-

Arts, Paris, which appears to be Bellini's preparatory drawing for (2); (4) a picture by Mantegna in the Stephen Courtauld Collection, of which an 18th century engraving exists (Borenius, *Four Italian Engravers*, pp. 52, 53). The present drawing is most nearly related to (1), (2) and (3), though not corresponding in detail. It has not the peculiar mannerisms of Parentino, whose name has been suggested, and might well be by the same hand as the drawing in the École des Beaux-Arts. For a discussion on the related material, see J. Byam Shaw in *Burlington Magazine*, XCIV, 1952, pp. 157 and 237."

PROVENANCE: Jan Pietersz. Zoomer (Lugt 1511); John Skippe; his descendants, the Martin family, including Mrs. A. C. Rayner-Wood; Edward Holland Martin; Skippe sale, London, Christie's, November 20–21, 1958, no. 37, pl. 5.

BIBLIOGRAPHY: Fritz Heinemann, *Giovanni Bellini e I Belliniani*, Venice [1962], p. 54 under no. 179.

EXHIBITIONS: London, Royal Academy, "Drawings by Old Masters," 1953, no. 21.

Robert Lehman

4 *St. Jerome in a Landscape*

Pen and brown ink. 7 × 8⅜ inches (17.8 × 21.3 cm.). Repaired breaks and small losses, especially at edges.

The very fact that this sheet is among the earliest examples of Italian landscape drawings contributes to the difficulty of placing it properly. While *St. Jerome in a Landscape* is exhibited here under the attribution of the owner, it was consistently ascribed to Piero di Cosimo by Berenson in his *Drawings of the Florentine Painters*; it was also accepted as such by Langton Douglas in his monograph on Piero. Recent critical opinion inclines to the authorship of an artist from Venice, or in any case the Veneto, and in addition to stylistic considerations, the easy, airy rendering of water, trees, and mountains does seem to indicate familiarity with this kind of terrain. The possibility, however, cannot be overlooked that the half-timbered buildings may be inspired by Northern models, known perhaps through prints. Puppi, who categorically rejected the attribution to Bellini and cited the winding vista of sea and mountains in the background of

Bartolomeo Montagna's painting of *St. Jerome* in the Brera, Milan, hesitantly included the Lehman sheet in his list of drawings by the Vicentine master. Heinemann, too, dismissed Bellini's name and apparently also Montagna's, noting only "la composizione ricorda Bartolomeo Montagna." Until more evidence accumulates, it is perhaps best to follow the catalogue of the Paris exhibition of the Lehman Collection and speak only of a Venetian master who was of the generation of Giorgione and influenced by Giovanni Bellini.

The landscape drawings in the Uffizi (Berenson, 1938, nos. 1858–1859, plausible as Piero di Cosimo), and the *St. Francis* in the Bonnat Collection at Bayonne (Berenson, 1938, no. 1848 B) were considered by Berenson in context with the Lehman landscape, but the drawings are actually quite different, sharing only the distinction of their earliness.

The saint writing before the entrance to his cell in a rocky cliff seems suitably identified as St. Jerome, although the name of St. John on Patmos has also been proposed.

PROVENANCE: Luigi Grassi (Lugt S. 1171b); sale, under the initials G. L. [Grassi], London, Sotheby's, May 13, 1924, no. 147, repr.

BIBLIOGRAPHY: Berenson, 1938, no. 1859 J, fig. 429 (as Piero di Cosimo); R. Langton Douglas, *Piero di Cosimo*, Chicago, 1946, p. 128, pl. LXXX; Jacob Bean, *Bayonne, Musée Bonnat, Les Dessins italiens de la collection Bonnat*, Paris, 1960, under no. 110; Berenson, 1961, no. 1859 J, fig. 346 (as Piero di Cosimo [?]); Fritz Heinemann, *Giovanni Bellini e I Belliniani*, Venice [1962], p. 286, no. V. 467; Lionello Puppi, *Bartolomeo Montagna*, Venice, 1962, p. 148, fig. 107.

EXHIBITIONS: Northampton, Smith College, Italian Drawings, 1941, no. 44; Paris, Lehman Collection, 1957, no. 112; Cincinnati, Lehman Collection, 1959, no. 201, repr.; New Haven, Yale University Art Gallery, "Paintings, Drawings and Sculpture Collected by Yale Alumni," 1960, no. 159, repr.

Robert Lehman

Giovanni Bellini, studio of

5 *The Last Supper*

Pen, point of brush, and brown ink, brown wash. 8¾ × 15⁵⁄₁₆ inches (22.2 × 39 cm.). Lined.

The existence of another drawing, identical in subject and measurements, in the British Museum

(*Catalogue of Drawings by Dutch and Flemish Artists*, II, 1923, p. 139, no. 17, as "David Teniers, II. After Gaudenzio Ferrari [?]"), points up the fame of this representation of the Last Supper. The name of Gaudenzio is clearly not applicable to the Morgan drawing, which is certainly Venetian in the manner in which it is drawn with the point of the brush and in the atmospheric treatment of the heads of the Apostles. In a general way, the composition has points of contact with a lost Bellini painting of *Christ at Emmaus*, known through an engraving by Pietro Monaco (active Venice, 1735–1775) and various painted copies (G. Gronau, *Giovanni Bellini*, Klassiker der Kunst, 1930, pp. 184–185). When Giles Robertson examined the drawing in 1963, he expressed the opinion that it is a post-Bellini work.

Christ Washing the Feet of the Disciples is a scene often combined with the Last Supper, but not usually as a view through a window as seen here. The Tietzes' omission of any mention of this drawing in their catalogue of Venetian drawings would appear to have been an oversight.

PROVENANCE: Marquess of Normanby (according to Charles Fairfax Murray); Charles Fairfax Murray; purchased by J. Pierpont Morgan in London, 1910.

BIBLIOGRAPHY: Fairfax Murray, I, no. 52, repr.; Fritz Heinemann, *Giovanni Bellini e I Belliniani*, Venice [1962], p. 235, no. V. 118 (perhaps by Benedetto Diana).

The Pierpont Morgan Library
No. I, 52

Antonio Pollaiuolo

Florence 1433–Rome 1498

6 *Study for a Projected Equestrian Monument to Francesco Sforza*

Pen and brown ink, light brown wash; dark brown wash in background. The outlines of horse and rider are pricked for transfer. 11³/₁₆ × 9⅝ inches (28.5 × 24.4 cm.). Various abrasions and losses; margins irregular.

This and the related study in the Graphische Sammlung at Munich (Inv. 1908:168) would seem to be those once owned by Vasari and described by him in the *Lives* (Milanesi, ed., III, p. 297) as the variant designs, found in Pollaiuolo's studio after his death,

for the monument Ludovico Sforza proposed to erect in commemoration of his father, Francesco Sforza. The drawings presumably were executed between 1480 and about 1485, that is, sometime between the date Ludovico became Regent in Milan and the time when Leonardo became involved in the ill-fated project. (Leonardo's clay model, produced in 1493, was destroyed during the French occupation in 1499, and no bronze was ever cast.)

It may be significant for the sequence of the two sheets that the outlines of the Lehman rider and horse were pricked for transfer but not the contours of the nude female beneath the horse. This figure, presumably the "Verona" of Vasari's description, that is, the personification of the city, is replaced by an armored warrior in the Munich composition where there are also numerous other alterations, including the prominent elevation of the rider's right arm.

Degenhart and Schmitt have recently suggested that the dark backgrounds in both the Lehman and Munich drawings were brushed in by Vasari himself. The fact that the background wash is not carried completely to the edge of the Lehman drawing is explained by them as an effort to make the New York drawing conform to the size of the Munich sheet.

PROVENANCE: Giorgio Vasari (?); Simon Meller; Philip Hofer.

BIBLIOGRAPHY: Giorgio Vasari, *Le Vite . . .*, Milanesi, ed., III, Florence, 1880, p. 297; Van Marle, *Italian Schools of Painting*, XI, p. 370; Simon Meller, "Pollaiuolo tervrajzai Francesco Sforza lovasszobrahoz," *Hommage à Alexis Petrovich*, Budapest, 1934, p. 204; Otto Kurz, "Giorgio Vasari's 'Libro de' Disegni,'" *Old Master Drawings*, XI, no. 45, 1937, p. 13; Berenson, 1938, p. 27, n. 4, no. 1908 A, fig. 78; Charles de Tolnay, *History and Technique of Old Master Drawings*, New York, 1943, p. 111, pl. 42; G. Colacicchi, *Antonio del Pollaiuolo*, Florence, 1945, pl. 77; Tietze, *European Master Drawings*, no. 13, repr.; Sergio Ortolani, *Il Pollaiuolo*, Milan [1948], pp. 169, 220–221, pl. 134 (useful summary of previous opinions); Peter Halm, Bernhard Degenhart, and Wolfgang Wegner, *Hundert Meisterzeichnungen aus der Staatlichen Graphischen Sammlung München*, Munich, 1958, p. 26; Berenson, 1961, p. 59, no. 1908 A, fig. 75; Bernhard Degenhart and Annegrit Schmitt, "Methoden Vasaris bei der Gestaltung seines 'Libro,'" in *Studien zur toskanischen Kunst, Festschrift für L. H. Heydenreich*, Munich, 1964, p. 58, fig. 12.

EXHIBITIONS: Buffalo, Master Drawings, 1935, no. 9, repr.; Northampton, Smith College, Italian Drawings,

1941, no. 15; Philadelphia, Masterpieces of Drawing, 1950–1951, no. 12, repr.; Paris, Lehman Collection, 1957, no. 119, pl. XLVIII; Cincinnati, Lehman Collection, 1959, no. 203, repr.

Robert Lehman

7 Seated Figure of a Prophet or Saint

Pen and brown ink, brown wash, heightened with white; pricked for transfer. 11 × 7⅞ inches (27.9 × 18.7 cm.).

The list of names of important artists that has been attached to this drawing through several centuries is a tribute to its interest and at the same time a witness to the continuous refining of our knowledge of *quattrocento* draughtsmanship. In the late eighteenth century, when Metz engraved it, it was described as Piero della Francesca. Popham included it in the great Italian exhibition of 1930 at Burlington House under the label "Attributed to Antonio Pollaiuolo," and this artist's name was attached to it without reserve in the much later Cincinnati exhibition of the Lehman Collection. Sir Kenneth Clark, in reviewing the Burlington House exhibition prior to the appearance of the catalogue in 1931, characterized the drawing as the "most important unpublished drawing of the mid-fifteenth century" and ascribed it "as possibly by Castagno," with whose school Berenson placed it in the 1938 edition of his catalogue of Florentine drawings. Berenson, however, added a qualifying statement, implying reservations that were also present in different guise in Byam Shaw's earlier attribution of the sheet to Francesco Botticini, the name accepted by K. T. Parker in the Oppenheimer catalogue. Berenson remarked, "but for quality it might be by him [Castagno]. Perhaps it is the pricking that suggests drawings for embroideries and inclines me to wonder whether it is not rather a copy and a faithful one, after Castagno by Raffaele dei Carli [Raffaellino del Garbo]."

A number of significant resemblances with other drawings by Raffaellino del Garbo, including No. 25 of the exhibition, suggest that the drawing may eventually rest with this artist's invention.

PROVENANCE: Nicholas Lanière (Lugt 2885); C. M. Metz; Henry Oppenheimer; Oppenheimer sale, London, Christie's, July 10, 1936, no. 38 (as Francesco Botticini).

BIBLIOGRAPHY: Metz, *Imitations of Drawings*, no. 7 (as Piero della Francesca); Kenneth Clark, "Italian Drawings at Burlington House," *Burlington Magazine*, LVI, 1930, p. 176, pl. B; J. Byam Shaw, "Francesco Botticini," *Old Master Drawings*, IX, no. 36, 1935, p. 59, n. 1; Berenson, 1938, no. 669 B, fig. 70; 1961, no. 669 B (as school of Castagno).

EXHIBITIONS: London, Royal Academy, Italian Art, 1930: commemorative drawings catalogue, 1931, no. 35, pl. XXX A (attributed to Antonio Pollaiuolo); Northampton, Smith College, Italian Drawings, 1941, no. 13; Cincinnati, Lehman Collection, 1959, no. 202, repr.; New Haven, Yale University Art Gallery, "Paintings, Drawings and Sculpture Collected by Yale Alumni," 1960, no. 154, repr.

Robert Lehman

Francesco del Cossa

Ferrara about 1435–Bologna 1477

8 Venus Embracing Cupid at the Forge of Vulcan

Pen and brown ink. 11 × 15⅞ inches (28 × 40.7 cm.). Small losses at corners.

The North Italian origin of the drawing is indisputable, but the specific locale and the artist that should be credited with its lively invention are less clear. By reason of its iconography, the drawing has, since its introduction into the literature by Roger Fry in 1906, been most often associated with the frescoes of the Palazzo Schifanoia at Ferrara and the name of Cossa and his assistants. Fry also mentioned in passing the name of Jacopo Bellini, and more lately Byam Shaw in the catalogue of the Royal Academy exhibition of 1953 suggested that there are some reminiscences of the early Giovanni Bellini.

The entry in the Columbia University exhibition catalogue of 1959 discussed the significance of the subject at length, remarking that the Vulcan-Venus episode could have been conceived as a pendant for the Mars-Venus fresco in the Schifanoia cycle. Vulcan's enclosure of Venus and Cupid on the little hill—perhaps the legendary *Venusberg* Fry suggested—is interpreted as a symbol of the marriage bond, the rabbits bespeaking fertility, the guardian peacock, marital fidelity, the embracing putti, mutual love. The bull at the upper left is the zodiacal sign of Taurus, which in company with the planet Venus rules the month of April; the infant Zephyrus blowing flowers before him is also an allusion to the season.

The Lehman drawing has no stylistic connection with the series of drawings in the Uffizi (Inv. 2321–2328 F; sometimes attributed to Quentin Massys) which Peter Meller has recently proposed as the work of Francesco Cossa on the basis of analogies with the Schifanoia frescoes (*Master Drawings*, III, 1965, pp. 3 ff.). No truly documented drawings by Cossa are known at present.

PROVENANCE: Jan Pietersz. Zoomer (Lugt 1511); John Skippe; his descendants, the Martin family, including Mrs. A. C. Rayner-Wood; Edward Holland Martin; Skippe sale, London, Christie's, November 20–21, 1958, no. 81, pl. 12.

BIBLIOGRAPHY: R. E. Fry, *Vasari Society*, first series, II, 1906–1907, no. 14 (as Ferrarese school); K. T. Parker, *North Italian Drawings*, London, 1927, no. 24, repr. (as style of Francesco Cossa); Eberhard Ruhmer, "Bernardo Parentino und der Stecher PP," *Arte Veneta*, XII, 1958, pp. 40–41, fig. 35 (as Parentino [?]); Moskowitz, ed., *Great Drawings*, I, no. 63, repr.; Winslow Ames, *Drawings of the Masters: Italian Drawings from the 15th to the 19th Century*, New York, 1963, p. 62, pl. 30.

EXHIBITIONS: London, Royal Academy, Italian Art, 1930: commemorative drawings catalogue, 1931, no. 147, pl. CXXVII (as school of Francesco Cossa); London, Royal Academy, "Drawings by Old Masters," 1953, no. 20, pl. 4; New York, Columbia Benefit Exhibition, 1959, no. 6, pl. 6.

Robert Lehman

Francesco di Simone Ferrucci, attributed to

Fiesole 1437–Florence 1493

9 *Page from a Sketchbook: Studies of a Kneeling Madonna, of St. Peter, of Faith and Charity, and of the Christ Child Standing on a Chalice*

Pen and brown ink over metalpoint, on pink prepared paper. 10¾ × 7⅝ inches (27.3 × 19.4 cm.).

Verso: Various pen studies of a Madonna and Child and of St. Sebastian.

This double-faced drawing is one of a group of twenty sheets scattered in a number of collections (Berlin, Chantilly, Dijon, Hamburg, the Louvre, the École des Beaux-Arts, Paris, and the British

Museum). Two of the sheets are dated 1487, one 1488, and stylistic evidence suggests that they are the working sketches of a Tuscan sculptor strongly influenced by Verrocchio. Some of the sheets were traditionally attributed to this sculptor, but the draughtsmanship is not his. Giovanni Morelli was the first to propose the name of the Verrocchiesque Francesco di Simone, and this attribution has been generally accepted. The drawings are close in style to a design in the Nationalmuseum in Stockholm that may well be Francesco di Simone's original study for his tomb of Alessandro Tartagni in S. Domenico, Bologna. On the other hand, certain of the inscriptions on the sheets seem to conflict with the thesis of Francesco's authorship. The vexed question is summed up by Popham and Pouncey in a full discussion of the sheets in the British Museum.

PROVENANCE: Lord Brownlow; Brownlow sale, London, Sotheby's, July 14, 1926, no. 17, repr. (recto); Philip Hofer, Cambridge, Massachusetts.

BIBLIOGRAPHY: Berenson, 1938, I, p. 48, n. 3; III, fig. 129 (recto, as Francesco di Simone); A. E. Popham and Philip Pouncey, *Italian Drawings in the Department of Prints and Drawings in the British Museum. The Fourteenth and Fifteenth Centuries*, I, London, 1950, pp. 39–40; Otto Kurz, "A Group of Florentine Drawings for an Altar," *Journal of the Warburg and Courtauld Institutes*, XVIII, 1955, pp. 35–46, fig. 18c (recto); Virch, *Baker Collection*, no. 3, repr. (recto and verso).

EXHIBITIONS: Boston, Museum of Fine Arts, "Art in New England," 1939, no. 208, pl. 88 (recto); Cambridge, Massachusetts, Fogg Art Museum, "Master Drawings Lent by Philip Hofer," 1940, no. 3 (as school of Verrocchio); Northampton, Smith College, Italian Drawings, 1941, no. 22 (as school of Verrocchio).

Walter C. Baker

Francesco di Giorgio di Martino

Siena 1439–Siena 1502

10 *A Kneeling Humanist Presented by Two Muses*

Pen and brown ink, brown wash and blue gouache, on vellum. 7¼ × 7⅝ inches (18.4 × 19.4 cm.).

Inscribed in pen and brown ink at lower left, *Franco Francia*; in the cartouche *Franco/Francia Bolognese*.

When this drawing came to light in the 1950s, it was attributed to Francesco di Giorgio by Philip Pouncey, Deputy Keeper of Prints and Drawings of the British Museum, which owns a manuscript on engineering and military subjects (1947-1-17-2[1-84]) by this versatile Sienese. Its relation to the figures appearing on various leaves of the British Museum manuscript is unmistakable, both from the point of view of types and of handling.

As was pointed out in the catalogue of the 1959 Columbia University benefit exhibition, the central devotional figure brings to mind the St. Thomas in the *Nativity* in the Pinacoteca, Siena, a signed painting of 1475; the same is true of the female figure on the left in the drawing and of the saint in the right rear of the painting. The Columbia catalogue also suggested that the "presentation in *trompe l'oeil*" might indicate that the artist had a sculptural project in mind, but the design was more likely intended for a painting or, not impossibly, intarsia. Mr. Pouncey in conversation proposed the attractive theory that the drawing could have been the model for an illusionistic painting of a donor to be placed rather high on a wall opposite a painting of the Madonna and Child of the donor's benefaction.

PROVENANCE: The Misses M. H., L. E., and M. D. Le Hunte; sale, Important Old Master Drawings and Paintings [including Le Hunte], London, Sotheby's, June 9, 1955, no. 42, repr.

EXHIBITIONS: Paris, Lehman Collection, 1957, no. 98, pl. XLIX; New York, Columbia Benefit Exhibition, 1959, no. 7, repr.

Robert Lehman

Sandro Botticelli

Florence 1444/1445–Florence 1510

11 *Fragment of an Adoration of the Magi*

Brown and white tempera on prepared linen. 12⅜ × 13¼ inches (31.5 × 33.7 cm.). Extensive repairs.

The Morgan Library's damaged but still impressive fragment of an Adoration of the Magi, and the two related pieces in the Fitzwilliam at Cambridge, made their way as a group through the collections of William Young Ottley, Sir Thomas Lawrence,

and William Russell under the name of Fra Filippo Lippi. Hermann Ulmann (*Sandro Botticelli*, Munich, 1893, p. 147) first published the New York drawing as probably Botticelli's own, but Berenson in 1903 referred to the larger Fitzwilliam fragment (then in the collection of James Knowles and apparently the only one Berenson knew at the time), as a copy and excluded it even from the school of Botticelli. Horne published the entire group in 1903 and again in 1909–1910 as copies after a lost *Adoration* by Botticelli, possibly the Palazzo Vecchio fresco that was destroyed at the time of Vasari's renovation. Yashiro in 1929 was the first to speak out unhesitatingly for Botticelli's authorship, regarding the fragments as parts of an original study for a projected altarpiece or fresco, and by 1938 Berenson was "more ready to accept them as Botticelli's own." Philip Pouncey is the latest critic to pronounce in favor of Botticelli's own hand. In his recent review of the Italian edition of Berenson's *Drawings of the Florentine Painters* in *Master Drawings*, he wrote, "As time passed Berenson evidently came to regret some of his early judgments of quality which do seem unnecessarily harsh. He has now completed his amends in the case of the beautiful fragments of an Adoration of the Magi, divided between the Fitzwilliam (561 A and B) and the Morgan Library (569)."

The most beautiful and least damaged portion of the Morgan fragment, the superbly delineated horses, recalls the greatest of all Adorations of fifteenth-century Florence, Leonardo's unfinished work. Elements in each of the three fragments can be associated with passages in Botticelli's unfinished *Adoration* in the Uffizi.

PROVENANCE: W. Young Ottley; Ottley sale, London, T. Philipe, June 13, 1814, no. 735; Sir Thomas Lawrence (Lugt 2445); William Russell; Russell sale, London, Christie's, December 11, 1884, no. 395; George Salting; Charles Fairfax Murray; purchased by J. Pierpont Morgan in London, 1910.

BIBLIOGRAPHY: Hermann Ulmann, *Sandro Botticelli*, Munich, 1893, p. 147; Herbert P. Horne, "A Lost 'Adoration of the Magi,' by Sandro Botticelli," *Burlington Magazine*, I, 1903, pp. 69, 70; Fairfax Murray, I, no. 5, repr.; Herbert P. Horne, *Sandro Botticelli, Painter of Florence*, London, 1908, p. 47; Herbert P. Horne, "A Lost *Adoration of the Magi* by Sandro Botticelli," *Burlington Magazine*,

XVI, 1909–1910, p. 40; Yukio Yashiro, *Sandro Botticelli*, Boston-London, 1929, pp. xxi, 241–242; Van Marle, *Italian Schools of Painting*, XII, pp. 23, 122; Berenson, 1938, p. 333, no. 569 A, fig. 202; Aldo Bertini, *I grandi maestri del disegno: Botticelli*, Milan, 1953, p. 10, pl. 13; Carlo L. Ragghianti, "Inizio di Leonardo, "*Critica d'Arte*, I, 1954, p. 117, fig. 65; Cambridge, Fitzwilliam Museum, *Fifteenth & Sixteenth Century Drawings*, 1960, under no. 19; Berenson, 1961, p. 150, no. 569 A, fig. 192; Philip Pouncey, review of Bernard Berenson, *I Disegni dei pittori fiorentini*, Milan, 1961, in *Master Drawings*, II, 1964, p. 283.

EXHIBITIONS: Toronto, Inaugural Exhibition, 1926, no. 28.

The Pierpont Morgan Library
No. I, 5

Francesco Francia

Bologna about 1450–Bologna 1517

12 *Judith and Holofernes*

Pen and brown ink, brown and green washes, some heightening with white, on vellum. 14⁵⁄₁₆ × 10¼ inches (36.3 × 26.1 cm.).

According to a letter of Raphael published in the 1841 annotated edition of Malvasia's *Felsina Pittrice* (I, p. 47), Francia executed a drawing of this subject for presentation to Raphael, and the fame of the composition is attested by the number of versions that survive. Of these, the present drawing and one in the Louvre from the collection of Baldinucci (Inv. 5606; 32.4 × 26 cm.) are of the best quality and very near in size. The relief style of drawing, which would be appropriate for a medal or coin, is in keeping with Francia's position as Director of the Mint at Bologna. A second drawing in the Louvre (R. F. 522) is an inferior copy, as is the red chalk version in the Albertina (Schönbrunner-Meder, II, no. 163). The fact that the Morgan drawing and those in the Louvre are executed on vellum, a more precious material than paper, is consistent with the tradition of a presentation drawing. Vasari dwells at some length on Francia's lost decoration of a room for Giovanni Bentivoglio that depicted the story of Judith and Holofernes.

PROVENANCE: Charles Fairfax Murray; purchased by J. Pierpont Morgan in London, 1910.

BIBLIOGRAPHY: Fairfax Murray, I, no. 94, repr.; Thieme-

Becker, XII, p. 323; *Metropolitan Museum of Art Bulletin*, January 1913, p. 17; Moskowitz, ed., *Great Drawings*, I, no. 81, pl. 81.

EXHIBITIONS: Buffalo, Master Drawings, 1935, no. 18, repr.; New York, Morgan Library, World's Fair, 1939, no. 63; 1940, no. 81; New York, Morgan Library, Fiftieth Anniversary Exhibition, 1957, no. 81.

The Pierpont Morgan Library
No. I, 94

Bernardino dei Conti

Pavia about 1450–Milan about 1525

13 *Head of a Man*

Black chalk with touches of red on lips, eyelid, and ear. 16 × 10⁹⁄₁₆ inches (40.6 × 26.8 cm.). Various losses and repairs, notably at left center and lower right.

This large-scale drawing, which must date around 1500, is a rather late manifestation of the tradition of the strict profile portrait favored earlier in the *quattrocento*. It has been assigned to a variety of other Milanese artists following in the wake of Leonardo, but it seems preferable to leave it with the label under which it was first published by K. T. Parker in 1927 until some objective evidence is forthcoming. Parker offered a plausible comparison with a signed and dated (1499) portrait of a cardinal by Bernardino dei Conti in the Gemälde-Galerie, Berlin-Dahlem, where a sitter of similar proportions is presented in rigid profile. The Jacquemart-André male profile portrait, likewise signed and dated (1500), might also be offered in evidence (Suida, p. 273, pl. 198). Ragghianti's suggestion of Pordenone's authorship is untenable.

PROVENANCE: Henry Oppenheimer; Oppenheimer sale, London, Christie's, July 13, 1936, no. 153, pl. 38 (as Ambrogio da Predis).

BIBLIOGRAPHY: K. T. Parker, *North Italian Drawings of the Quattrocento*, London, 1927, no. 68, pl. 68; W. E. Suida, *Leonardo und sein Kreis*, Munich, 1929, p. 173 (as Ambrogio da Predis); C. L. Ragghianti, *Commenti di critica d'arte*, Bari, 1946, p. 226, fig. 6 (as Pordenone).

EXHIBITIONS: London, Royal Academy, Italian Art, 1930: commemorative drawings catalogue, 1931, no. 188, pl. CLVIII B; New York, Columbia Benefit Exhibition, 1959, no. 11, pl. XVII.

Benjamin Sonnenberg

25

Bartolomeo Montagna

Near Brescia or Vicenza about 1450–Vicenza 1523

14 Nude Man Standing beside a High Pedestal

Brush and black pigment heightened with cream-white on paper originally blue-gray, now faded. 15¾ × 10⁹⁄₁₆ inches (40 × 25.8 cm.). Irregularly trimmed, some water stains, particularly at left, and scattered holes; left corner missing. Lined.

Inscribed in pen and brown ink at lower center, *21*; at lower right, *vene*.

The identity of the tall, spare nude figure is obscure. He resembles the type the artist casts in the role of St. Sebastian (cf. the *Enthroned Madonna and Saints*, the painting in the Accademia Carrara, Bergamo, repr. Lionello Puppi, *Bartolomeo Montagna*, Venice, 1962, pl. 17). The grapes spilling over the edge of the vase at the top of his wand, which is lashed with a palm, might be thought to have Dionysiac implications, although the ascetic severity of the figure seems to oppose such an interpretation. Classical ancestry is certainly ultimately implicit in the figure's nudity and pose.

As far as could be determined at present, the drawing is not linked with any painted composition and is illustrated here for the first time. It may have been the remote inspiration of the engraving *Man with an Arrow* by Bartolomeo's son Benedetto (Arthur M. Hind, *Early Italian Engraving*, VII, London, 1948, pl. 750, no. 15). Bartolomeo Montagna was the leading Renaissance painter of the school of Vicenza.

Private Collection

Leonardo da Vinci

Vinci 1452–Cloux 1519

15 Studies for a Nativity

Pen and brown ink, over preliminary sketches in metalpoint, on pink prepared paper. Ruled lines added in black chalk. 7⅝ × 6⁷⁄₁₆ inches (19.3 × 16.2 cm.).

Verso: Slight geometric sketches in pen and brown ink.

In these sketches of the Virgin kneeling in humility before the Christ Child, who lies on the ground, Leonardo investigated a theme that was to become the *Madonna of the Rocks*, where the Virgin kneels facing the spectator, her right hand raised in benediction over the seated Infant Jesus. The sketches at the center and at the lower left corner of the sheet, where the Virgin raises both arms in devotional wonder, are close to a small composition study on a sheet at Windsor (repr. Popham, pl. 160). These sketches are related to a design by Leonardo that must have been brought at least to the stage of a complete cartoon, for several painted copies have survived. Recent controversy over the chronology of the Paris and London versions of the *Madonna of the Rocks* makes it difficult to date the Metropolitan drawing. If, as had generally been assumed, the Louvre *Madonna of the Rocks* was the picture commissioned in Milan in 1483, then the drawing may be dated at about that time. If, however, the National Gallery *Madonna*, a work finished in Leonardo's late style, was the altarpiece originally commissioned in 1483, and the Louvre picture was painted in Florence before the artist's departure for Milan, as Martin Davies and Kenneth Clark contend, then the present drawing might be appreciably earlier and assignable to Leonardo's first Florentine period.

PROVENANCE: J. G. Legrand; J. Allen Smith; Thomas Sully; Francis T. S. Darley; Thomas Nash; purchased by the Metropolitan Museum from Nash in New York, 1917.

BIBLIOGRAPHY: Bryson Burroughs, "Drawings by Leonardo da Vinci on Exhibition," *Metropolitan Museum of Art Bulletin*, October 1918, pp. 214–217, repr. p. 215; Aldo de Rinaldis, *Storia dell' opera pittorica di Leonardo da Vinci*, Bologna, 1926, p. 51, pl. 19; Popp, *Leonardo*, p. 37, pl. 19; *Commissione Vinciana*, II, no. 40; Suida, *Leonardo*, pp. 51, 270, pl. 49; Bodmer, *Leonardo*, repr. p. 149; Berenson, 1938, no. 1049 C, fig. 484; Metropolitan Museum, *European Drawings*, I, repr. no. 8; Popham, *Leonardo*, pp. 69, 149, pl. 159; Tietze, *European Master Drawings*, p. 42, no. 21, repr. p. 43; Clark, *Leonardo*, p. 42, pl. 20; Heydenreich, *Leonardo*, I, p. 183; II, pl. 34; Berenson, 1961, no. 1049 C, fig. 475; Charles de Tolnay, "Quelques dessins inédits de Léonard de Vinci," *Raccolta Vinciana*, fascicule XIX, 1962, pp. 110–111, fig. 13 (the hitherto unpublished verso of the sheet); Moscowitz, ed. *Great Drawings*, I, no. 153, repr.; Bean, *100 European Drawings*, no. 3, repr.

EXHIBITIONS: Philadelphia, Masterpieces of Drawing 1950–1951, no. 21, repr.

The Metropolitan Museum of Art Rogers Fund, 17.142.1

16 Head of a Man

Pen and brown ink, over traces of black chalk. $4\frac{5}{8} \times 2\frac{1}{16}$ inches. (11.6 × 5.2 cm.). Edges of sheet torn irregularly. Lined.

In this profile of an old man with sharply aquiline nose, down-slanted mouth, and knotted brow, Leonardo has brought the "ideal" head almost to the limits of the grotesque. It is not likely that this is a portrait or caricature; it is more probably a conscious recollection of the ideal portrait of Darius carved by Leonardo's master, Verrocchio. Verrocchio's bas-relief, sent by Lorenzo the Magnificent to the king of Hungary, is now lost, but the profile is recorded in a Della Robbia workshop terracotta relief in the Berlin Museum (repr. Leo Planiscig, *Andrea del Verrocchio*, Vienna, n.d., pl. 38). A highly finished early drawing by Leonardo in the British Museum (repr. Popham, pl. 129) must have been directly inspired by the Verrocchio relief. Popham dates the British Museum drawing about 1480, and places the Metropolitan's sketch, where the powerful features of the imaginary Darius are recorded in a more forceful and schematized fashion, about 1490. Leonardo's truly grotesque heads, exaggerated works of pure fantasy, were, on the whole, done a good deal later in his career.

PROVENANCE: Sir Peter Lely (Lugt 2092); purchased by the Metropolitan Museum in London, 1909.

BIBLIOGRAPHY: *Vasari Society*, first series, VII, 1911–1912, no. 2, repr.; Berenson, 1938, no. 1049 D; Metropolitan Museum, *European Drawings*, I, repr. no. 10; Popham, *Leonardo*, pp. 64, 145, pl. 140 C; Berenson, 1961, no. 1049 D, fig. 495; Bean, *100 European Drawings*, no. 4, repr.

The Metropolitan Museum of Art
Rogers Fund, 10.45.1

17 Allegory

Pen and brown ink. $7\frac{5}{16} \times 5\frac{3}{8}$ inches (20.2 × 13.3 cm.).

Inscribed in pen and brown ink in the artist's hand, reading from right to left: *El ramarro fedele allomo vedēdo quello adormētato cōbatte cholla bisscia esse vede nōlla potere vincere core sopa, il volto dellomo ello dessta acchioche essa bisscia no noffenda lo adormentato homo.*

Verso: Pen studies for the *Masque of Danae*.

This mysterious allegorical representation of a man asleep, with his head resting perilously near the entangled group of a lizard struggling with a serpent, is open to as many interpretations as Leonardo's own reversed left-handed inscription will allow. Popham, who entitles the composition *Allegory of the Lizard Symbolizing Truth*, offers the following translation of the text: "The lizard faithful to man, seeing him asleep, fights with the serpent and, if it sees it cannot conquer it, runs over the face of the man and thus wakes him in order that the serpent may not harm the sleeping man." The circular form of the design suggests that it may have been intended for an allegorical emblem, probably done for the Sforza court in Milan. The drawing can be dated with some precision, for the verso of the sheet has presumably contemporaneous studies by Leonardo for the setting of the *Masque of Danae*, composed by Baldassare Taccone and presented on January 31, 1496, in the house of Giovanni Francesco Sanseverino, Conte di Cajazzo.

PROVENANCE: J. G. Legrand; J. Allen Smith (according to an inscription on the old mount that reads: *Souvenir d'amitié a J. allen Smith par J. G. Legrand en floréal an 9.*); Thomas Sully; Francis T. S. Darley; Thomas Nash; purchased by the Metropolitan Museum from Nash in New York, 1917.

BIBLIOGRAPHY: Bryson Burroughs, "Drawings by Leonardo da Vinci on Exhibition," *Metropolitan Museum of Art Bulletin*, October 1918, pp. 214–217; Popp, *Leonardo*, p. 39, pl. 27; Bodmer, *Leonardo*, repr. p. 233; *Commissione Vinciana*, III, no. 106; Berenson, 1938, no. 1049 B; Metropolitan Museum, *European Drawings*, I, repr. no. 9; Popham, *Leonardo*, pp. 59, 135, pl. III; Heydenreich, *Leonardo*, I, p. 60; II, p. 64, pl. 81; Berenson, 1961, no. 1049 B; Bean, *100 European Drawings*, no. 5, repr.

The Metropolitan Museum of Art
Rogers Fund, 17.142.2

18 Study of a Bear Walking

Silverpoint on pinkish buff prepared paper. $4\frac{1}{16} \times 5\frac{1}{4}$ inches (10.3 × 13.4 cm.).

Beyond his preoccupation with horses, Leonardo made drawings of only a few other animals. Of these, the bear seems to have interested him as much as any other animal with the possible exception of the dog and the cat.

The Lehman *Bear Walking* is one of a group of

three silverpoint studies from nature by Leonardo that reappeared in the 1930s. They had been lost sight of since the time of Sir Thomas Lawrence, to whom they had belonged at the beginning of the nineteenth century, along with a dozen or so other genuine Leonardo sheets. The two other drawings, one a study of the head of a bear, and the second a sheet of studies of the paws of a dog or wolf, belong to Lt. Col. N. R. Colville, London. At Windsor there are four remarkable studies of the dissection of the hind foot of a bear (Clark 12372–75), which, as William Wright first pointed out (*Burlington Magazine*, XXXIV, 1919, p. 203), are to be linked with Leonardo's statement in the plan for his projected anatomical treatise, "Then I will discourse of the hands of each animal to show in what they vary; as in the bear, which has the ligatures of the toes joined above the instep" (Windsor Anatomical Ms. B.; J. B. Richter, *The Literary Works of Leonardo*, II, Oxford, 1939, p. 822). Some such thought must have already been generating in the artist's mind when he made the separate sketch of the forepaw on this sheet. It is conceivable that the bear studied in the Lehman drawing was the one that the artist later dissected.

Popham, while commenting on the difficulty of dating the silverpoint studies from nature, placed the drawings in this medium in Leonardo's earlier Florentine period; Clark suggested they were done in Milan about 1490. The pen sketch of a bear in the *Codice Atlantico* at the Ambrosiana Library, Milan (fol. 98r) is thought to be considerably later. A bear also occurs in the *Allegory* in the Louvre (Popham, *Leonardo*, pl. 110a).

PROVENANCE: Sir Thomas Lawrence (Lugt 2445); L. V. Randall.

BIBLIOGRAPHY: Kenneth Clark, "Leonardo da Vinci, Study of a Bear Walking," *Old Master Drawings*, XI, no. 44, 1937, pp. 66–67, pl. 65; A. E. Popham, "The Drawings at the Burlington Fine Arts Club," *Burlington Magazine*, LIX, 1937, p. 87; Berenson, 1938, no. 1010 J; Popham, *Leonardo*, p. 55, no. 78 B; Berenson, 1961, no. 1049 E.

EXHIBITIONS: Philadelphia, Masterpieces of Drawing, 1950–1951, no. 22, repr.; London, Royal Academy, "Leonardo da Vinci, Quincentenary Exhibition," 1952, no. 41; Paris, Lehman Collection, 1957, no. 106, pl. LI; Cincinnati, Lehman Collection, 1959, no. 206, repr.

Robert Lehman

19 *Head of the Virgin*

Black and colored chalks. 8 × 6⅛ inches (20.3 × 15.6 cm.). Repairs at right margin.

Illegible inscription in pen and brown ink at upper left.

This highly finished drawing, heightened in colored chalks, is certainly related to and is possibly a study for the head of the Virgin in Leonardo's *Virgin and Child with St. Anne*, now in the Louvre, a picture probably painted during Leonardo's second stay in Milan and datable about 1508–1510. At Windsor there is a much freer black chalk study that is universally accepted as a study for the head of St. Anne in the same picture. All the authorities cited in the bibliography, with Berenson first and foremost, have proclaimed the present drawing to be an original by Leonardo and a study for the Louvre picture. No doubts as to its authorship have been published by Leonardo scholars, but its conspicuous omission from several recent publications on the artist and his drawings seems to reflect critical skepticism in certain circles. The problem is difficult, because though Leonardo is known to have made considerable and very original use of various colored chalks, no other example that can be surely attributed to him has survived. The Milanese followers of Leonardo were quick to adopt this technical innovation of their master; many Lombard head studies, which are often directly inspired by Leonardo, are known, but none of them approaches the exceptional quality or the poetic power of this head, subtly modeled in light and shade. Corrections or restorations by a later hand may account for the dark passages at nostril and lips. An old copy of the drawing is in the Albertina (Wickhoff, *Albertina*, p. CLXXXV, S.R. 62).

PROVENANCE: Sir Charles Greville (Lugt 549); George Guy, Fourth Earl of Warwick (Lugt 2600); Warwick sale, London, Christie's, May 20–21, 1896, no. 213; Dr. Ludwig Mond, London; Lady Melchett; Melchett sale, London, Sotheby's, May 23, 1951, no. 7, repr. frontispiece, bought by the Metropolitan Museum.

BIBLIOGRAPHY: Berenson, 1903, no. 1045; J. P. Richter, *The Mond Collection*, II, London, 1910, p. 323, pl. XIX; Gustavo Frizzoni, "La Raccolta Mond ed opere attinenti alla medesima," *Rassegna d'Arte*, XI, 1911, p. 43, fig. 6; Venturi, IX, Part I, fig. 138; Osvald Sirén, *Leonardo da Vinci*, New Haven, 1916, p. 137; Aldo de Rinaldis, *Storia* dell' *opera pittorica di Leonardo da Vinci*, Bologna, 1926, p. 235, pl. 69; Berenson, 1938, no. 1045, fig. 514; Theodore Rousseau, *Metropolitan Museum of Art Bulletin*, December 1951, repr. cover; Berenson, 1961, no. 1049 D–I, fig. 499.

EXHIBITIONS: London, Grosvenor Gallery, "Drawings by the Old Masters and Artists of the British School," 1877–1878, no. 675.

The Metropolitan Museum of Art
Harris Brisbane Dick Fund, 51.90

Ercole de' Roberti

Ferrara about 1456–Ferrara 1496

20 *The Flagellation*

Pen and brown ink, minutely worked with point of brush and brown wash, heightened with white. 14¾ × 9¼ inches (38.5 × 23.5 cm.). Some staining and abrasion.

Opinion on the authorship of *The Flagellation* differs. It has been customarily linked for over a century with Ercole de' Roberti, but it is possible that Milanese sources as well as Ferrarese should be investigated. Berenson in a communication to the owner once mentioned the possibility of Bramantino. The pronounced *sfumato* effect in the head of the Christ seems unusual in the context of the linearism of the contours. There appears to be a *pentimento* in the torso of the figure of Christ.

PROVENANCE: August Grahl (Lugt 1199); Marius de Zayas; Alfonse Kann.

BIBLIOGRAPHY: *Grahl Collection* [Leipzig, n.d.], pl. 340.

EXHIBITIONS: Buffalo, Master Drawings, 1935, no. 13, repr.; Cincinnati, Lehman Collection, 1959, no. 209, repr.

Robert Lehman

Filippino Lippi

Prato 1457/1458–Florence 1504

21 *Christ and the Magdalene: Figure Studies for a Noli me tangere*
Verso: *Youth with a Sword and Kneeling Youth with a Staff*

Leadpoint, heightened with white, on gray prepared paper. The figure of the standing youth on the verso is executed mainly in silverpoint. 10⅝ × 7¹⁵⁄₁₆ inches (27 × 20.1 cm.).

Scharf has proposed that a number of Filippino's drawings of this type (his figs. 147–151), particularly those like the present example, which have figure studies on either side, were leaves from a sketchbook. The relationship between the Morgan sheet and several in the British Museum (especially 1895–9–15–454), which have almost identical measurements and are executed on similarly colored grounds with the same strong patterning of rhythmic crosshatching, is sufficiently strong to warrant the assumption of a common origin. Scharf dated the series before 1490, but the drawings may be somewhat later in view of the nervous intricacy and unrest of the drapery.

None of the four figures of this sheet can be associated with a known painting, but the tall gentle Christ, with his long hoe, and the trembling Magdalene (it would seem to be she though the Gothic monstrance is admittedly an unusual substitution for the ointment jar) suggest that the artist was here contemplating the figures of a *Noli me tangere* and would later bring them into spatial rapport. The Magdalene, who lacks any softness of face or figure, may have been studied from a male model. The long-haired youth in the short jerkin, sketched in dynamic pose on the verso, could well be a spectator in some elaborately staged Adoration. He does, in fact, somewhat resemble the figure crouching on a ledge in the *Adoration of the Magi* of 1496 in the Uffizi.

PROVENANCE: Licht; Czeckowiczka; Czeckowiczka sale, Leipzig, Boerner's, May 12, 1930, nos. 98, 99; Mark Oliver; C. R. Rudolf; purchased by the Pierpont Morgan Library in London, 1951.

BIBLIOGRAPHY: Van Marle, *Italian Schools of Painting*, XII, p. 361, note; Alfred Scharf, *Filippino Lippi*, Vienna, 1935, no. 228, p. 124; Berenson, 1938, no. 1348 A, fig. 253; Morgan Library, *Third Fellows Report*, 1952, pp. 59–62, repr.; Berenson, 1961, no. 1353 F.

EXHIBITIONS: London, P. & D. Colnaghi, "Exhibition of Old Master Drawings," 1951, no. 1, frontispiece; New York, Morgan Library, Fiftieth Anniversary Exhibition, 1957, no. 82, pl. 50; New York, Wildenstein, "Masterpieces," 1961, no. 59, repr.

The Pierpont Morgan Library
Purchased with the assistance of the Fellows, 1951.1

22 Studies of Two Male Figures

Metalpoint, heightened with white, on pink prepared paper. 9¹¹⁄₁₆ × 8½ inches (24.6 × 21.6 cm.).

Verso: Metalpoint studies of hands, on pink prepared paper.

This study of two young models, one posed as St. Sebastian with his hands tied behind his back, the other seated with a book in hand, is a typical example of a Florentine studio drawing. Although the figures cannot be discovered in these particular poses in a painted work by Filippino, they must have been studied with a larger composition in mind. Filippino, like so many of his Florentine contemporaries, has used metalpoint on prepared paper to outline the figures and to indicate inner modeling; white gouache highlights give further plasticity to form. The present drawing was attributed to Raffaellino del Garbo by J. P. Heseltine, who once owned the sheet, but this very characteristic work by Filippino has appeared under that artist's name in all three editions of Berenson's work on Florentine drawings.

PROVENANCE: Lord de l'Isle; J. P. Heseltine; Henry Oppenheimer; Oppenheimer sale, London, Christie's, July 10–14, 1936, no. 112, repr., bought by the Metropolitan Museum.

BIBLIOGRAPHY: Hermann Ulmann, "Raffaellino del Garbo," *Repertorium für Kunstwissenschaft*, XVII, 1894, p. 113; Hermann Ulmann, "Bilder und Zeichnungen der Brüder Pollajuoli," *Jahrbuch der Königlich Preussischen Kunstsammlungen*, XV, 1894, p. 244; Berenson, 1903, no. 1349; *Original Drawings by Old Masters of the Italian School Forming Part of the Collection of J. P. H[eseltine]*, London, 1913, no. 22, repr.; Alfred Scharf, *Filippino Lippi*, Vienna, 1935, p. 124, no. 229, pl. 101, fig. 148; Berenson, 1938, no. 1353 B; Metropolitan Museum, *European Drawings*, I, repr. no. 5; Tietze, *European Master Drawings*, p. 32, no. 16, repr. p. 33; Mongan, *One Hundred Drawings*, p. 24, repr. p. 25; Berenson, 1961, no. 1353 B; Bean, *100 European Drawings*, no. 6, repr.

EXHIBITIONS: London, Royal Academy, Italian Art, 1930: commemorative drawings catalogue, 1931, no. 46, pl. XL; Philadelphia, Masterpieces of Drawings, 1950–1951, no. 18, repr.

The Metropolitan Museum of Art
Harris Brisbane Dick Fund, 36.101.1

Vittore Carpaccio

Venice 1460/1465–Venice about 1526

23 Study of a Youth in Armor

Point of brush and gray wash, heightened with white, on blue paper. 7⁷⁄₁₆ × 7¹⁄₁₆ inches (18.9 × 18 cm.).

Carpaccio has drawn a young model dressed in a full suit of armor and posed as though he were on horseback, his arm raised with indication of a spear in his gloved hand. The artist may have intended to use this study in a composition representing the youthful St. George fighting the dragon, but the saint is quite differently represented in the series of canvases painted for the Scuola di S. Giorgio degli Schiavoni about 1502–1508. The drawing may be a rejected preparatory drawing for the St. George series, and Lauts dates it on stylistic grounds in the first decade of the sixteenth century. Typically Venetian is Carpaccio's use of the point of the brush, rather than metalpoint or pen and ink, to delineate form and to study the details of the suit of armor.

PROVENANCE: Purchased by the Metropolitan Museum in New York, 1954.

BIBLIOGRAPHY: Agnes Mongan, "Venetian Drawings in America," *Atti del XVIII Congresso Internazionale di Storia dell' Arte, 1955*, Venice, 1956, p. 304, fig. 201; Giuseppe Fiocco, *Carpaccio*, Novara, 1958, pl. 100; Jan Lauts, *Carpaccio, Paintings and Drawings*, London, 1962, pp. 273–274, no. 37, pl. 122; Bean, *100 European Drawings*, no. 7, repr.

EXHIBITIONS: London, P. & D. Colnaghi, "Old Master Drawings," 1954, no. 12, repr.; Venice, Palazzo Ducale, "Mostra di Vittore Carpaccio," 1963, no. 14 in the catalogue of drawings, repr.

The Metropolitan Museum of Art
The Elisha Whittelsey Collection, 54.119

Piero di Cosimo, attributed to

Florence 1462–Florence 1521

24 Head of a Young Woman

Metalpoint heightened with white, on pale blue prepared paper. 5⅝ × 5 inches (14.3 × 12.7 cm.).

It was J. Byam Shaw who proposed the attribution to Piero di Cosimo of this beautiful head of a young woman, possibly a study for the Virgin in a Nativity or Adoration. The use of metalpoint with white heightening is typical of Florence in the late fifteenth century and, as Byam Shaw suggested, the shape of the head, the heavy-lidded eyes, the tinge of Flemish influence, and the Filippinesque style of draughtsmanship would seem to point to the early phase of the activity of Piero di Cosimo. However, no drawings in metalpoint by Piero that can be definitely connected with pictures have survived, and the attribution to Piero of this fine sheet remains speculative.

BIBLIOGRAPHY: "Londra: Mostre di maestri antichi," *Emporium*, CXL, 1964, p. 90, repr.

EXHIBITIONS: London, Royal Academy, "Drawings by Old Masters," 1953, no. 34; London, P. & D. Colnaghi, "Exhibition of Old Master Drawings," 1964, no. 6, repr. frontispiece.

Walter C. Baker

Raffaellino del Garbo

Florence about 1466–Florence 1524

25 The Angel of the Annunciation

Pen and brown ink, brown wash, heightened with white on brown washed paper. Contours pricked for transfer. Diameter 3¾ inches (9.7 cm.). Lined.

Vasari reports that Raffaellino del Garbo, hard-put to find commissions for large-scale panels, made many designs for ecclesiastical embroideries. The finish and the size of this roundel, with an elegant three-quarter-length figure of the angel of the Annunciation, go far to suggest that it may be a design for such an embroidery; the fact that the contours have been carefully pricked for transfer seems further evidence of the purpose of the design. A number of similar pricked and highly finished drawings by Raffaellino in the Uffizi and the British Museum have been generally accepted as embroidery patterns.

PROVENANCE: Sir Charles Eastlake, London; J. P. Richter, London; purchased by the Metropolitan Museum in London, 1912.

BIBLIOGRAPHY: Berenson, 1938, no. 766 A; Metropolitan Museum, *European Drawings*, I, repr. no. 12; Berenson, 1961, no. 766 E; Bean, *100 European Drawings*, no. 8, repr.

The Metropolitan Museum of Art
Rogers Fund, 12.56.5a

Francesco Morone

Verona 1471–Verona 1529

26 The Virgin and Child with St. Roch and St. Sebastian

Drawn with the point of brush in brown, and further modeled in white and blue gouache. 9⅝ × 14¾ inches (24.4 × 37.5 cm.). The sheet is pieced at left and right, the left third overlapping the central section, and it in turn overlapping the right addition. The left piece is slightly off register, as can be seen in the area of the molding of the throne. Stains, losses, and abrasions, especially in the lower quarter; upper corners replaced.

Inscribed at lower right in a relatively late hand, *Fra^{co} Moron*.

Originally the group of the Virgin and Child of this composite sheet was flanked on the right by the Infant John the Baptist, as demonstrated by the remnant of the saint's scroll inscribed AGNVS DEI ECCE / PECATA. The substitution of the figure of St. Sebastian as the recipient of the Christ Child's blessing was undoubtedly made by the draughtsman himself since the saint's head is in part executed on the paper of the central section. Just why the figure of St. Roch, like Sebastian a saint invoked against the plague, was cut away and then rejoined slightly off register is hard to say. Very likely there had been previous alterations, since St. Roch's gaze is not directed to the action of the central group as might be expected. It is obvious that the artist made a number of corrections and changes at various stages of his work, especially in the contour of the St. Sebastian. No painting of the subject is mentioned in Wittkower's basic checklist of Morone's works in "Studien zur Geschichte der Malerei in Verona, III," *Jahrbuch für Kunstwissenschaft*, IV, 1927, pp. 199–212. Tietze-Conrat, who first drew attention to the drawing, considered it an early work.

The simple sincerity of religious expression inherent in the assembled figures is in accord with

Vasari's report of the Veronese artist as a devout, gentle personality who requested that he be carried to his grave in the habit of a Franciscan friar.

BIBLIOGRAPHY: E. Tietze-Conrat, "Francesco Morone in America," *Art in America*, XXXI, 1943, p. 87, fig. 3; Moskowitz, ed., *Great Drawings*, I, no. 82, repr.; Winslow Ames, *Drawings of the Masters: Italian Drawings from the 15th to the 19th Century*, New York, 1963, p. 112, pl. 80.

EXHIBITIONS: Paris, Lehman Collection, 1957, no. 115; Cincinnati, Lehman Collection, 1959, no. 211, repr.

Robert Lehman

Baccio della Porta, called Fra Bartolomeo

Florence 1472–Florence 1517

27 *The Adoration of the Magi*

Pen and brown ink. 11 × 9½ inches (28 × 24.2 cm.).

A related drawing in the Uffizi (repr. Berenson, 1938, no. 235, fig. 439) shows Fra Bartolomeo's concern, at a fairly early date in his career, with the composition of an elaborate Adoration of the Magi, in which the landscape background with horsemen and figures reclining on a suggestion of ruined architecture reveals the influence of Leonardo's unfinished *Adoration of the Magi* now in the Uffizi. No surviving picture by Fra Bartolomeo records the result of these investigations. The present drawing, an exceptionally complete pen design by the artist, was mistakenly attributed to Raphael by Samuel Woodburn, but it appears under the name of Fra Bartolomeo in the first edition of Berenson's study of Florentine draughtsmanship.

PROVENANCE: The Earls Spencer (Lugt 1530); Sir Thomas Lawrence (Lugt 2445); Samuel Woodburn; Woodburn sale, London, Christie's, June 7, 1860, no. 738 (as Raphael); Sir John Charles Robinson; Marquess of Northampton, Castle Ashby; Northampton sale, London, Christie's, May 1, 1959, no. 1, repr.

BIBLIOGRAPHY: Berenson, 1903, no. 438; *Vasari Society*, first series, X, 1914–1915, no. 2, repr.; Hans von der Gabelentz, *Fra Bartolommeo* . . . , II, Leipzig, 1922, p. 135, no. 315; Berenson, 1938, no. 438; Berenson, 1961, no. 459 H; Virch, *Baker Collection*, no. 6, repr.

EXHIBITIONS: London, Royal Academy, "Drawings by Old Masters," 1953, no. 50.

Walter C. Baker

28 *The Virgin with the Holy Children*

Pen and brown ink over black chalk. 7¼ × 6¼ inches (18.4 × 15.9 cm.).

Verso: Child at extreme right on recto is traced through; sketch of another child.

Gabelentz associated this drawing with three at the Uffizi (Gabelentz 151r and v; 174r) and two at Windsor (Gabelentz 73 and 874) as part of a sequence of pen sketches for a projected picture, presumably a tondo representing the standing Virgin holding the Christ Child, with the Infant Baptist at the left and combinations of angelic and saintly attendants varying from scheme to scheme. If Gabelentz is correct in placing these drawings about 1505, they follow closely on the Frate's resumption of artistic activity as head of the monastery workshop of S. Marco at Florence in 1504. It will be recalled that after he had retired to S. Marco in 1500 to become a monk, he had given up painting for some years.

PROVENANCE: Count Ottolini; J. P. Heseltine (Lugt 1507); Henry Oppenheimer; Oppenheimer sale, London, Christie's, July 10, 1936, no. 31, pl. 6.

BIBLIOGRAPHY: F. Knapp, *Fra Bartolommeo* . . . , Halle a. S., 1903, p. 314, no. 4; Berenson, 1903, no. 430; Hans von der Gabelentz, *Fra Bartolommeo* . . . , II, Leipzig, 1922, p. 133, no. 307; Berenson, 1938, no. 459 G; Popham–Wilde, *Italian Drawings at Windsor*, p. 193, under no. 113; Berenson, 1961, no. 459 G.

EXHIBITIONS: London, Royal Academy, Italian Art, 1930: commemorative drawings catalogue, 1931, no. 190, pl. CLX B.

Robert Lehman

29 *The Virgin and Child Enthroned, with Saints and Musical Angels*

Black and white chalk on light brown paper. 14⅜ × 10⅞ inches (36.6 × 27.6 cm.), arched at the top. Watermark: fruit (Briquet 7392). The silhouetted arched top has been extended to form a rectangle. Several small stains.

Despite the fact that Berenson in the 1903 edition of his catalogue had attributed this compositional sketch for an elaborate altarpiece to Fra Paolino, Fairfax Murray in 1912 persisted in the traditional attribution to Fra Paolino's master. Berenson in 1938 added the qualifying remark "close to Fra

Bartolommeo and possibly his," and repeated the same entry in the last edition of his catalogue. In favor of the attribution to Fra Bartolomeo, it can be remarked that unquestioned drawings by Fra Paolino like the Uffizi studies (Berenson, 1961, figs. 420 and 422), which are preparatory for the *Crucifixion* in the cloister of S. Spirito, Siena, and the *Adoration of the Magi* in S. Domenico, Pistoia, have an affinity that is not shared by the Morgan drawing. As is the case with almost any artist's work, Fra Bartolomeo's pen drawings present far fewer problems of authenticity than those executed in chalk.

PROVENANCE: George Skene (according to Fairfax Murray); Sir John Charles Robinson (Lugt 1433); Charles Fairfax Murray; purchased by J. Pierpont Morgan in London, 1910.

BIBLIOGRAPHY: Berenson, 1903, no. 1820 (as Fra Paolino); Fairfax Murray, IV, no. 11, repr., Berenson, 1938, no. 1827 A; Berenson, 1961, no. 1827 A (under Fra Paolino).

The Pierpont Morgan Library
No. IV, 11

30 *Approach to a Mountain Village with Horsemen on the Road*

Pen and brown ink. 11¾ × 8³⁄₁₆ inches (29.8 × 20.6 cm.).

This drawing and the four listed immediately below once formed part of an album containing forty-one landscape studies by Fra Bartolomeo. The album, broken up and sold at auction in 1957, bore the arms of the Florentine art historian Cavaliere Gabburri (1675–1742) on its frontispiece and had a title page that attributed all the drawings to Andrea del Sarto. However, the characteristic pen style of these spirited sketches, which are among the earliest pure landscape studies in European art, proclaims them to be the work of Fra Bartolomeo.

Another view of the picturesque mountain hamlet represented in the present drawing occurs in one of the Gabburri sheets acquired by Count Seilern at the 1957 auction. The Seilern sketch shows the steep-roofed cottages and conical haystacks lining both sides of the road from a more distant and perhaps slightly different vantage point—certainly

not from the opposite direction as described in the Sotheby catalogue—and is of peculiar interest in that it was used for the landscape in the background of Giuliano Bugiardini's *Rape of Dinah* in the Kunsthistorisches Museum at Vienna, a picture Vasari describes as begun by Fra Bartolomeo and finished by Bugiardini. This relationship, the only instance in which one of the landscapes from the Gabburri album has been directly connected with a painting, was the discovery of Isolde Härth ("Zu Landschaftszeichnungen Fra Bartolommeos und seines Kreises," *Mitteilungen des Kunsthistorischen Institutes in Florenz*, IX, 1959, pp. 124–130. Reference kindly supplied by Count Seilern).

PROVENANCE: Fra Paolino da Pistoia, Florence; Suor Plautilla Nelli; Convent of St. Catherine, Piazza S. Marco, Florence; Cavaliere Francesco Maria Nicolò Gabburri, Florence; William Kent (?); private collection, Ireland; sale, London, Sotheby's, November 20, 1957, no. 1, repr. (catalogue by C[armen] G[ronau]).

BIBLIOGRAPHY: John Fleming, "Mr. Kent, Art Dealer, and the Fra Bartolommeo Drawings," *Connoisseur*, CXLI, 1958, p. 227 (discussion of the provenance of the whole group); Ruth W. Kennedy, "A Landscape Drawing by Fra Bartolommeo," *Smith College Museum of Art Bulletin*, no. 39, 1959, pp. 1–12 (discussion of the whole group).

Robert Lehman

31 *A Small Town on the Crest of a Slope*

Pen and brown ink. 11 × 8⅝ inches (27.9 × 21.8 cm.). Watermark: close to Briquet 7382.

PROVENANCE: See No. 30 above. Sale, London, Sotheby's, November 20, 1957, no. 7, repr. (catalogue by C[armen] G[ronau]).

BIBLIOGRAPHY: See No. 30 above.

The Metropolitan Museum of Art
Rogers Fund, 57.165

32 *A View of Fiesole from the Mugnone Valley*

Pen and brown ink. 8⁷⁄₁₆ × 11³⁄₁₆ inches (21.4 × 28.4 cm.).

PROVENANCE: See No. 30 above. Sale, London, Sotheby's, November 20, 1957, no. 14, repr. (catalogue by C[armen] G[ronau]).

BIBLIOGRAPHY: See No. 30 above.

Curtis O. Baer

33 *Monastery Church and Well among the Trees*

Pen and brown ink. $11\frac{1}{16} \times 8\frac{7}{16}$ inches (28.1×21.4 cm.). Very small gray stain at lower left corner of verso. Watermark: fruit (Briquet 7386).

Verso: View of the same monastery from another direction in pen and brown ink.

PROVENANCE: See No. 30 above. Sale, London, Sotheby's November 20, 1957, no. 17, repr. (catalogue by C[armen] G[ronau]).

BIBLIOGRAPHY: See No. 30 above. Morgan Library, *Ninth Fellows Report, 1958–1959*, pp. 88–91, repr.

The Pierpont Morgan Library
Gift of the Fellows, 1957.18

34 *Wooded Approach to a Town*

Pen and brown ink. $8\frac{3}{8} \times 11\frac{9}{16}$ inches (21.2×29.3 cm.).

PROVENANCE: See No. 30 above. Sale, London, Sotheby's, November 20, 1957, no. 26, repr. (catalogue by C[armen] G[ronau]).

BIBLIOGRAPHY: See No. 30 above. Virch, *Baker Collection*, no. 8, repr.

Walter C. Baker

Amico Aspertini

Bologna 1475–Bologna 1552

35 *Bacchanalian Scene*

Black chalk, heightened with white, on brown washed paper. $10\frac{7}{8} \times 16\frac{3}{4}$ inches (27.6×42.6 cm.). Three diagonal creases at lower margin. Lined.

This is a free and fanciful copy after Mantegna's engraving *The Bacchanal with a Wine Press* (Arthur M. Hind, *Early Italian Engraving*, Part II, V, London, 1948, p. 13, no. 4). Aspertini, *uomo capriccioso e di bizzarro cervello*, according to Vasari, has transformed Mantegna's stately, measured composition into a curiously animated and rather sinister scene of alcoholic debauch. The artist traveled over all Italy, it is said, "copying every painting and relief, the good with the bad," but whatever he recorded seems to have been metamorphosed by the energy of his own strange, mad style. Three sketchbooks, one in a fragmentary state at Schloss Wolfegg, South Germany, and two in the British Museum, remain to testify to Aspertini's assiduity in recording motifs or compositions that interested him. The overwhelming majority of these drawings are free copies after antique sculpture, but one is not surprised to find that in the second British Museum sketchbook he has noted down two compositions by his ardently classicizing predecessor Mantegna (Phyllis Pray Bober, *Drawings after the Antique by Amico Aspertini*, London, 1957, pp. 81, 87, fig. 113). The present drawing may be contemporary with or perhaps a little later than these sketches, which Mrs. Bober dates about 1540.

At the time of its acquisition in 1908 by the Metropolitan Museum, the drawing was attributed to Lorenzo Leonbruno, a minor figure known for his imitations of Mantegna. Philip Pouncey, in 1958, was the first to point out that the drawing is a characteristic work of Aspertini.

PROVENANCE: Jonathan Richardson Senior (Lugt 2184); purchased by the Metropolitan Museum in London, 1908.

BIBLIOGRAPHY: "Recent Acquisitions of Drawings," *Metropolitan Museum of Art Bulletin*, December 1908, p. 224; Bean, *100 European Drawings*, no. 9, repr.

The Metropolitan Museum of Art
Rogers Fund, 08.227.27

Michelangelo Buonarroti

Caprese 1475–Rome 1564

36 *Studies for the Libyan Sibyl*
Verso: *Study of Legs, a Knee, and of a Small Seated Figure*

Red chalk (recto). Black chalk (verso). $11\frac{3}{8} \times 8\frac{3}{8}$ inches (28.9×21.4 cm.). Spots of brown wash at lower right. Triangular section at right margin replaced.

Inscribed in pen and light brown ink at lower left, *di M . . . nglo bonarroti.*; unidentified paraph in pen and darker brown ink at lower center. Inscribed on verso in pen and brown ink at upper right, *58.*; at lower center, *n⁰. 21.*

This celebrated sheet bears on the recto a series of studies from a nude male model for the figure of the

Libyan Sibyl that appears on the frescoed ceiling of the Sistine Chapel. The Sistine frescoes were commissioned in 1508 and finally unveiled in 1512. In the principal and highly finished drawing dominating the sheet Michelangelo has studied the turn of the sibyl's body, the position of the head and arms; in the fresco the sibyl turns to close a large book on a ledge behind her. The left hand of the figure is studied again below, as are the left foot and toes. A study of the sibyl's head, possibly the first drawing on the sheet, appears at the lower left, and a rough sketch of the torso and shoulders are immediately above it. A closely related drawing in the Ashmolean Museum at Oxford (Berenson, 1961, no. 1562, fig. 577) has red chalk studies for the sibyl's right hand and of the boy holding a scroll behind her. On the same sheet at Oxford occur studies for the slaves intended for the tomb of Julius II. The conjunction of studies for the Sistine ceiling and the tomb of Julius II gives evidence that the Libyan Sibyl, part of the very last phase of Michelangelo's work on the Sistine ceiling, was contemporary with the first plans for the ill-fated tomb. An old copy of the verso of the Metropolitan Museum's drawing with a few variants, possibly by a Northern artist, is in the Uffizi (repr. Paola Barocchi, *Michelangelo e la sua scuola. I Disegni di Casa Buonarroti e degli Uffizi*, Florence, 1962, no. 268, pl. CCCLXIII).

PROVENANCE: Aureliano de Beruete, Madrid; purchased from Beruete's widow by the Metropolitan Museum in Madrid, 1924.

BIBLIOGRAPHY: Karl Frey, *Die Handzeichnungen Michelagniolos Buonarroti*, I, Berlin, 1909, pp. 2–4, pl. 4 (recto), pl. 5 (verso); Bryson Burroughs, "Drawings by Michelangelo for the Libyan Sibyl," *Metropolitan Museum of Art Bulletin*, January 1925, pp. 6–14, repr. p. 8 (verso), p. 9 (recto); A. E. Brinckmann, *Michelangelo Zeichnungen*, Munich, 1925, p. 33, no. 32, pl. 32; Berenson, 1938, no. 1544 D, fig. 631 (recto); Metropolitan Museum, *European Drawings*, I, repr. no. 16 (recto), no. 17 (verso); Tietze, *European Master Drawings*, p. 76, no. 38, repr. p. 77 (recto); Mongan, *One Hundred Drawings*, p. 28, repr. p. 29 (recto); Charles de Tolnay, *Michelangelo*, II, *The Sistine Ceiling*, Princeton, 1955, pp. 61, 204, no. 46, pl. 80 (recto); verso discussed p. 209, no. 13 A, pl. 236 (the author does not accept the verso as Michelangelo's work); Ludwig Goldscheider, *Michelangelo Drawings*, London, 1951, no. 30; Parker, *Ashmolean Catalogue*, II, p. 141; Luitpold Dussler, *Die Zeichnungen des Michelangelo*, Berlin, 1959, pp. 183–184, no. 339, pl. 39 (recto); verso discussed p. 183, no. 339, pl. 174 (the author does not accept the verso as Michelangelo's work); Berenson, 1961, no. 1544 D, fig. 564 (recto), fig. 565 (verso); Moscowitz, ed., *Great Drawings*, I, no. 192, repr.; Bean, *100 European Drawings*, no. 10 (recto), repr.

EXHIBITIONS: Philadelphia, Masterpieces of Drawing, 1950–1951, no. 32, repr.

*The Metropolitan Museum of Art
Purchase, Joseph Pulitzer Bequest, 24.197.2*

37 David Slaying Goliath

Black chalk, a few extraneous touches of red chalk on I, 32a and I, 32d, traces of ruled gold margin at upper edge of I, 32a, left edge of I, 32c, and upper edge of I, 32d. I, 32a: $2\frac{3}{4} \times 4\frac{3}{8}$ inches (7×11.1 cm.); I, 32b: $2\frac{1}{16} \times 3\frac{1}{4}$ inches (5.2×8.2 cm.); I, 32c: $2 \times 2\frac{11}{16}$ inches (5×6.8 cm.); I, 32d: $2\frac{13}{16} \times 3\frac{1}{2}$ inches (7.2×8.7 cm.). Lined with transparent paper; I, 32a is creased across lower quadrant, and a loss at the lower left corner has been repaired.

Verso: Architectural members in black chalk.

These small fragments, so clearly stages in the evolution of the same idea, were at one time almost certainly part of the same sheet of paper although they obviously have been separate since the days of Sir Joshua Reynolds, whose mutilated mark appears in the lower left corner of each. The presence of similar ruled architectural elements in black chalk on the verso of each seems further to support the assumption that they were originally one piece of paper.

The drawings have always been accepted as Michelangelo's although authorities have differed as to their date and the purpose for which they were made. Tolnay, who summarizes all previous opinions, agrees with Thode that they were used by Daniele da Volterra for his painting *David and Goliath*, which is now in the Louvre (repr. Tolnay, V, pls. 184–185); he dates them around 1542–1545. His suggested sequence of execution (32b, 32a, 32d, 32c) seems the logical one, as does his conclusion that the related sketches of Samson Slaying the Philistine, on a sheet at Oxford, grew out of the Morgan sketches. The soft black chalk in which they are executed was the favored medium of Michelangelo's late period.

PROVENANCE: Sir Joshua Reynolds (Lugt 2364); Breadalbane (according to Fairfax Murray); Leighton (according to Fairfax Murray); Charles Fairfax Murray; purchased by J. Pierpont Morgan in London, 1910.

BIBLIOGRAPHY: Fairfax Murray, I, no. 32, repr.; Karl Frey, *Die Handzeichnungen Michelagniolos Buonarroti*, Berlin, 1909–1911, no. 76a–d; H. Thode, *Michelangelo*, III, Berlin, 1908–1913, no. 367; Berenson, 1938, no. 1544 E; Ludwig Goldscheider, *Michelangelo Drawings*, London, 1951, nos. 106–107; Parker, *Ashmolean Catalogue*, II, p. 169 under no. 328; Luitpold Dussler, *Die Zeichnungen des Michelangelo*, Berlin, 1959, p. 118, no. 188, repr.; Charles de Tolnay, *Michelangelo*, V, *The Final Period*, Princeton, 1960, p. 199, no. 207; Berenson, 1961, no. 1544 E.

EXHIBITIONS: Toronto, Inaugural Exhibition, 1926, no. 34.

The Pierpont Morgan Library
No. I, 32 a–d

Niccolò Giolfino

Verona 1476–Verona 1555

38 *The Betrayal of Christ*

Brush and brown wash, heightened with white gouache, over traces of black chalk, on greenish paper. 9¼ × 10½ inches (23 × 26.5 cm.). Small hole at lower left corner; crease along lower margin.

Inscribed in pen and brown ink at lower right, *Il. Giolfino, Fece. :C:* Inscribed in pen and brown ink in another hand at lower left, *Giottino* (?), *La Pittura á in Fio . . .* (rest illegible; written over a further inscription that has been erased).

The traditional attribution of this drawing to the Veronese painter Giolfino is stylistically convincing, and, at least from the time of Strong's publication of the drawings then at Wilton House, the sheet has been connected with a fresco by the artist in the church of S. Bernardino at Verona representing the Arrest of Christ. Drawings by Giolfino are extremely rare; indeed the present example could be considered unique until the reappearance last year in London of a stylistically and technically similar sheet bearing studies of allegorical figures in medallions (sale, London, Sotheby's, November 12, 1964, no. 110, repr.).

PROVENANCE: Earls of Pembroke; Pembroke sale, London, Sotheby's, July 5–10, 1917, no. 395, bought by the Metropolitan Museum.

BIBLIOGRAPHY: Strong, *Wilton House Drawings*, Part I, repr. no. 4.

The Metropolitan Museum of Art
Hewitt Fund, 19.76.17

Cesare da Sesto

Sesto Calende 1477–Milan 1523

39 *Two Leaves from a Sketchbook*

Two of a total of twenty-four leaves, until recently mounted in an early nineteenth-century album bound in brown calf, with gold and blind tooling, also containing a series of ten smaller leaves by another sixteenth-century Italian hand. The album has now been dismembered and the leaves mounted separately in the interest of their preservation.

Adam and Eve; Two Male Figures. Pen and brown ink, red chalk. 7½ × 5⅝ inches (19.1 × 14.2 cm.). Old pagination *12.* Verso: Various pen and ink studies, including Venus and Mars, Adam and Eve, and a grotesque.

The Judgment of Solomon; Virgin and Child. Pen and brown ink, red chalk. 7⅜ × 5⁹⁄₁₆ inches (18.8 × 14.2 cm.). Old pagination *21.* Verso: Pen and ink studies of David and Goliath, Judith and Holofernes, Virgin and Child, and grotesques.

The sketchbook from which these leaves came must have been one used by the Milanese artist in Rome, probably during the second decade of the century —certainly before his departure for Messina in 1514—since it contains so many reminiscences of then new works of Michelangelo and of Raphael. The Eve of page 12, for example, clearly is inspired by the figure in the *Fall of Man* on the ceiling of the Stanza della Segnatura.

On the evidence of the rendering of the tree from which Eve has just plucked the apples in the Morgan composition, the beautiful drawing of a tree at Windsor (Clark 12417), once thought to be by Leonardo himself, has been recognized as Cesare's work. It is supposed that Cesare must have been in direct contact with Leonardo, presumably about 1507–1510; the great Florentine's influence is obvious in Cesare's delicate penwork throughout the Morgan sketchbook which, according to Fairfax Murray, was even at one time attributed to Leonardo himself.

The scene of Solomon's Judgment displays Cesare's typical blend of motifs from Michelangelo and Raphael, the seated Solomon recalling the former's Sistine sibyls and *ignudi*, and the executioners, Raphael's soldiers in the *Massacre of the Innocents* as engraved by Marcantonio. The Virgin and Child at the lower right is one of a number of such studies in the sketchbook, sometimes dependent on Leonardo, sometimes, as here, on Raphael.

PROVENANCE: Charles Fairfax Murray; purchased by J. Pierpont Morgan in London, 1910.

BIBLIOGRAPHY: Fairfax Murray, II, pp. 5–6, nos. 38, 47, repr.; Gustavo Frizzoni, "Certain Studies by Cesare da Sesto in Relation to his Pictures," *Burlington Magazine*, XXVI, 1914–1915, pp. 187–194, pls. 1–3; Gustavo Frizzoni, "Rivelazioni della Galleria Cook," *Rassegna d'Arte*, XIV, 1914, pp. 126, 130; Francesco Valeri, *La Corte di Lodovico Il Moro*, Milan, 1913–1923, p. 573; Joseph Meder, *Die Handzeichnung, ihre Technik und Entwicklung*, Vienna, 1923, p. 125, n. 3; Kenneth Clark, *Drawings of Leonardo da Vinci at Windsor Castle*, I, Cambridge, 1935, p. 56 under no. 12417; Thieme-Becker, XXX, p. 535; Jacob Bean, *Bayonne, Musée Bonnat, Les Dessins italiens de la collection Bonnat*, Paris, 1960, under no. 152.

EXHIBITIONS: Los Angeles County Museum, "Leonardo da Vinci," 1949, no. 88.

The Pierpont Morgan Library
Nos. II, 38, 47

Giorgio da Castelfranco, called Giorgione

Castelfranco Veneto about 1478–Venice 1510

40 *Landscape with a Seated Old Man*

Pen and brown ink, brown wash, on brownish paper. 7⅜ × 10¼ inches (18.7 × 26.1 cm.). Slight smudges of red chalk at lower center; top right and lower left corners missing; holes at left and lower margin.

This fine landscape drawing was first attributed to Giorgione by Fröhlich-Bum, and this quite plausible suggestion has been accepted by the Tietzes, who pointed out that the draughtsmanship corresponds to Giorgione's style of about 1505. A contemporary document does indeed testify to the existence of pen drawings by Giorgione. The seated nude old man is possibly a representation of the penitent St. Jerome; as for the landscape, it is a composite of various natural and architectural ele-

ments, somewhat crowded together in a fashion that recalls the late *quattrocento*. The Tietzes have pointed out that in Rennes there is a copy of the right half of the landscape without the seated figure.

PROVENANCE: Padre Sebastiano Resta, Milan; Monsignor Giovanni Matteo Marchetti, Bishop of Arezzo; Cavaliere Marchetti of Pistoia; John, Lord Somers (Lugt 2981).

BIBLIOGRAPHY: Lili Fröhlich-Bum, "Venezianische Landschaftszeichnungen, Giorgione, Giulio Campagnola, Schiavone, Savoldo," *Belvedere*, I, 1930, p. 86, pl. 65/2; Tietze, *Venetian Drawings*, no. 713, pl. XLIX.

EXHIBITIONS: Montreal, Five Centuries of Drawings, 1953, no. 50, repr.

S. Schwarz Collection

Vincenzo Catena

Venice (?) about 1480–Venice after 1531

41 *Study of Drapery*

Black chalk and brown wash, heightened with white, on blue-green paper. 7¼₆ × 7¾₆ inches (18 × 18.6 cm.).

Elaborate study for the intricate folds of the upper part of the garment worn by the Angel Gabriel in an *Annunciation* by Catena. The picture, formerly in the church of S. Maria della Misericordia in Carpi, is now in the Municipal Museum of that town (repr. Giles Robertson, *Vincenzo Catena*, Edinburgh, 1954, no. 22, pl. 19). Robertson dates the panel about 1515 or shortly thereafter. Mr. Scholz's drawing had been attributed to G. B. Moroni and to Savoldo, but in 1956 Creighton Gilbert established its connection with the picture at Carpi. This beautiful drapery study is the only drawing that can as yet be attributed with certainty to Catena.

PROVENANCE: Pancaldi; Alessandro Maggiori (Lugt 3005b; pen inscription on verso: *Aless. Maggiori comprò a Bologna dal sa / cerdote Pancaldi il giorno [tre] fcb: del 1796*); Comte Rey de Villette (Lugt S. 2200a).

BIBLIOGRAPHY: Creighton Gilbert, "A Drawing by Catena," *Burlington Magazine*, XCVIII, 1956, p. 373, fig. 32; "Italian Drawings from the Collection of Janos Scholz," *Metropolitan Museum of Art Bulletin*, May 1965, p. 338, repr.

EXHIBITIONS: Oakland, Scholz Exhibition, 1956, no. 68 (as Moroni); Venice, Scholz Exhibition, 1957, no. 10, repr.; Bloomington, Scholz Exhibition, 1958, no. 12, repr.; Oakland, Scholz Exhibition, 1959, no. 18; Newark, Old Master Drawings, 1960, no. 13, repr.; Hamburg, Scholz Exhibition, 1963, no. 37, pl. 76; New Haven, Scholz Exhibition, 1964, no. 34.

Janos Scholz

Gaudenzio Ferrari

Valdúggia in Piemonte about 1480–Milan 1546

42 *Angel Playing a Violoncello*

Black chalk and brown wash, heightened with white. 14⅞ × 9⅜ inches (37.7 × 23.3 cm.). All four corners trimmed diagonally, large brown stain at upper left. Lined.

The single figure of the angel cellist, diaphanously brushed in Gaudenzio's characteristic manner, was part of the artist's preparation for the decoration of the cupola of the cathedral at Saronno. The same figure occurs at the lower right in the *Concert of Angels* at Munich (Inv. 2660), a compositional study made in the early stages of the Lombard artist's planning for the Saronno commission, which he executed in 1534–1535.

PROVENANCE: John Skippe; his descendants, the Martin family, including Mrs. A. D. Rayner-Wood; Edward Holland Martin; Skippe sale, London, Christie's, November 20–21, 1958, no. 93, pl. 14.

BIBLIOGRAPHY: Peter Halm, Bernhard Degenhart, and Wolfgang Wegner, *Hundert Meisterzeichnungen aus der Staatlichen Graphische Sammlung München*, Munich, 1958, under no. 58.

EXHIBITIONS: Birmingham, City Museum and Art Gallery, "Art Treasures of the Midlands," 1934, no. 220.

Private Collection

43 *The Conversion of St. Paul*

Black chalk, brown wash, heightened with white, on blue-green paper. 10⅝ × 14⅜ inches (27 × 36.3 cm.). Upper right corner replaced.

The abbreviated black chalk notations of heads and hands, and above all the lavish, pictorial use of white heightening, are characteristic of Gauden-zio's style as a draughtsman. Curved lines at upper right and left delimit the composition, which cannot be connected with a surviving work by this prolific narrative painter. The drawing was first attributed to Gaudenzio by Philip Pouncey.

EXHIBITIONS: Oakland, Scholz Exhibition, 1956, no. 28; Bloomington, Scholz Exhibition, 1958, no. 27, repr.; Hamburg, Scholz Exhibition, 1963, no. 53, pl. 15; New Haven, Scholz Exhibition, 1964, no. 36.

Janos Scholz

Lorenzo Lotto

Venice about 1480–Loreto 1556

44 *Draped Male Figure Reaching Upward*

Black chalk; squared in red chalk. 9⅜ × 6¹⁵⁄₁₆ inches (23.8 × 17.6 cm.). Repaired at upper left corner.

Verso: Black chalk head of a man, unfortunately effaced in the course of recent restoration of the sheet.

Study for the figure of an Apostle who appears at the lower left of Lotto's *Assumption of the Virgin* in the church of S. Maria Assunta at Celana near Bergamo, a picture signed and dated 1527 (repr. Berenson, *Lotto*, 1956, pl. 206). In 1934 Kieslinger published the portrait head formerly on the verso of the sheet as a study by Titian related to heads in his Pesaro Madonna in the Frari, but the Tietzes restored the designs on both recto and verso to Lotto, connecting the drapery study with the Celana altarpiece.

PROVENANCE: Giuseppe Vallardi (Lugt 1223); Franz Kieslinger, Vienna.

BIBLIOGRAPHY: Franz Kieslinger, "Tizian-Zeichnungen," *Belvedere*, XII, 1934–1937, p. 173, pl. 183 (verso); Tietze, *Venetian Drawings*, no. 779, pl. LXXXIX, 1 (verso) and 2 (recto); Anna Banti and Antonio Boschetto, *Lorenzo Lotto*, Florence, n.d., p. 81, pl. 147 (recto), pl. 148 (verso); Berenson, *Lotto*, 1955, pp. 95, 130, pl. 204 (recto), pl. 203 (verso); Berenson, *Lotto*, 1956, pp. 69, 97, pl. 204 (recto), pl. 203 (verso); Philip Pouncey, *Lotto disegnatore*, Vicenza, 1965, pp. 12–13, pl. 8.

EXHIBITIONS: Venice, Palazzo Ducale, "Mostra di Lorenzo Lotto," 1953, p. 183, no. 3; Venice, Scholz Exhibition, 1957, no. 11, repr. (recto); Bloomington, Scholz Exhibition, 1958, no. 28, repr. (recto); Oakland, Scholz Exhibition, 1959, no. 29.

Janos Scholz

45 *St. Martin Dividing His Cloak with a Beggar*

Brush and gray-brown wash, heightened with white and some cream wash, over black chalk. 12¼ × 8½ inches (31.2 × 21.7 cm.). Tear repaired at upper right.

Inscribed, possibly signed, in pen and brown ink on verso, *. . . entius. Lotus*

Schilling was the first to publish this design, the most monumental of the relatively few surviving drawings by Lotto. Pouncey, who like Schilling dates the sheet about 1530, has pointed out that both the asymmetrical composition, which seems to demand a pendant, and the steep perspective suggest that the drawing is a study for one of a pair of organ shutters. The example of Pordenone's panels with St. Martin and St. Christopher, painted in 1528 for S. Rocco in Venice, comes to mind, and they may indeed have influenced Lotto (see No. 52 of this exhibition).

BIBLIOGRAPHY: Edmund Schilling, "A Signed Drawing by Lorenzo Lotto," *Gazette des Beaux-Arts*, VIᵉ période, XLI, 1953, pp. 277–279, figs. 1, 2; Berenson, *Lotto*, 1955, p. 163, pl. 348; Berenson, *Lotto*, 1956, p. 124, pl. 348; Philip Pouncey, *Lotto disegnatore*, Vicenza, 1965, pp. 13–14, pl. 11.

EXHIBITIONS: Montreal, Five Centuries of Drawings, 1953, no. 53, repr.; Newark, Old Master Drawings, 1960, p. 23, repr.

S. Schwarz Collection

Bernardino Luini

Lombardy 1480/1485–Lombardy 1532

46 *St. Lawrence before the Prefect of Rome*

Pen and brown ink, brown wash, heightened with white; contours pricked for transfer. 7½ × 9½ inches (19.1 × 24.1 cm.).

The contours of this design, in which the facial types and the rather frozen gestures are so characteristic of Luini, are pricked for transfer, perhaps to a small predella panel. The scene represented has been described by Ottino Della Chiesa as St. Lawrence before Pope Sixtus II, but the seated male figure does not wear a papal crown and holds in his right hand what appears to be the fasces, symbol of Roman secular authority. More probably the com-position represents the Prefect of Rome calling on St. Lawrence to deliver up the treasure of the Church.

BIBLIOGRAPHY: Angela Ottino Della Chiesa, *Bernardino Luini*, Novara, 1956, p. 147, no. 29.

EXHIBITIONS: Oakland, Scholz Exhibition, 1956, no. 55; Bloomington, Scholz Exhibition, 1958, no. 25, repr.; Detroit, Drawings of the Italian Renaissance, 1960, no. 30, repr.; Hamburg, Scholz Exhibition, 1963, no. 89, pl. 14; New Haven, Scholz Exhibition, 1964, no. 39.

Janos Scholz

Baldassare Peruzzi

Siena 1481–Rome 1536

47 *The Holy Family with Saints, including St. Michael, and Donor*

Pen and brown ink, brown wash on paper tinted light brown. 7⁷⁄₁₆ × 5⅝ inches (18.9 × 14.2 cm.). Loss at lower right corner, sharp cut extending into design at upper right. Lined.

Inscribed in an old hand in pen and brown ink at lower left, undeciphered.

This drawing was traditionally ascribed to Sodoma until about 1950, when Pouncey properly attributed it to another Sienese artist, Baldassare Peruzzi, whose career as painter and architect was crowned by his appointment as architect of St. Peter's in succession to Raphael. Pouncey regards the drawing as a rather late example of Peruzzi's draughtsmanship.

PROVENANCE: The Earls Spencer (Lugt 1532); Charles Fairfax Murray; purchased by J. Pierpont Morgan in London, 1910.

BIBLIOGRAPHY: Fairfax Murray I, no. 44, repr. (as Sodoma).

The Pierpont Morgan Library No. I, 44

Raffaello Santi, called Raphael

Urbino 1483–Rome 1520

48 *The Agony in the Garden*

Pen and brown ink, brown wash; traced with stylus and also fully pricked. 8⅞ × 10⁷⁄₁₆ inches (22.6 × 26.5 cm.).

No watermark. Extensive repairs of breaks and losses. The drawing has recently been relined with transparent paper.

Inscribed on verso in pen and brown ink, *Timoteo Viti*.

Much of the original beauty of this now damaged drawing was lost in the processes of tracing, pricking, and pouncing, when it served as the cartoon for one of the predella panels of the Metropolitan Museum's *Madonna of S. Antonio*, the altarpiece painted by Raphael for the convent church of S. Antonio da Padova in Perugia about the time he attained his majority (1504–1505). The drawing has always been properly attributed to Raphael although the execution of the predella panel itself has on occasion been attributed to the hand of an assistant working after Raphael's design.

Recent laboratory examination of the predella panel and a tracing of the drawing's pricked outlines has furnished incontrovertible evidence that the Morgan drawing is the working cartoon. A few discrepancies between the correspondence of the outlines of the painting and those of the drawing are accounted for by the fact that in those passages where the pricked line has broken through, the edges of the paper along the breaks have been drawn together in slight distortion of the original spatial relationships. The chalice seen at the upper right in the drawing does not now show in the painting, but its outlines are visible under X-ray.

PROVENANCE: Viti-Antaldi (according to Fairfax Murray); Frederick, Lord Leighton (according to Fairfax Murray); Charles Fairfax Murray; purchased by J. Pierpont Morgan in London, 1910.

BIBLIOGRAPHY: Passavant, *Raphaël et son père*, II, p. 29; Fairfax Murray, I, no. 15, repr.; Fischel, p. 91, no. 66, pl. 66; Paul Schubring, *Der Cicerone*, XV, 1923, pp. 3 ff.; *Metropolitan Museum of Art Bulletin*, March 1933, pp. 58–59; Harry B. Wehle, *The Metropolitan Museum of Art: A Catalogue of Italian, Spanish and Byzantine Paintings*, New York, 1940, pp. 119–120; Ulrich Middeldorf, *Raphael's Drawings*, New York, 1945, p. 33, pl. 20.

EXHIBITIONS: Toronto, Inaugural Exhibition, 1926, no. 39, repr.; New York, Morgan Library, World's Fair, 1939, no. 67; 1940, no. 85.

The Pierpont Morgan Library
No. I, 15

49 *Madonna and Child with the Infant St. John*
Verso: *Nude Male Figure*

Red chalk (recto). Pen and brown ink (verso). 8 13/16 × 6¼ inches (22.4 × 15.4 cm.). Paper stained at lower left and center of recto, abraded at lower right of recto. Horizontal fold at center.

Inscribed in pen and brown ink at lower left, *1509.* (?); in pen and brown ink at lower right, *Raf: . . . .* Inscribed on verso in the artist's hand in pen and brown ink at lower right, *Carte de . . .* (the rest illegible); in pen and brown ink at lower left, *5.89/4 66/4 H. . . .*

This recently rediscovered drawing is a composition study for the *Madonna im Grünen* (*Madonna in the Meadow*) in the Kunsthistorisches Museum in Vienna, which bears a date that can be read as 1505 or 1506. Painted for Raphael's Florentine friend and patron Taddeo Taddei, the picture remained in the Palazzo Taddei in Florence until 1662, when it was purchased by the Archduke Ferdinand Karl and brought to Austria. Several of Raphael's preparatory drawings for the picture have survived. A double-faced sheet in the Albertina (Fischel, nos. 115, 116) bears pen sketches of alternative poses for the three figures, and the figure of the Infant Baptist is represented both standing and kneeling. In a pen drawing in the Devonshire Collection at Chatsworth (Fischel, no. 117), the Baptist is studied standing and also kneeling to embrace the Christ Child. A drawing at the Ashmolean Museum in Oxford (Fischel, no. 118), executed with the point of a brush and pale brown wash, comes close to the picture as executed, but the Metropolitan's drawing is the last in the sequence of preparatory drawings. There is, however, one significant variant between the drawing and the picture. The Madonna's right arm, free in the drawing, is covered in the painting with rather heavy drapery. In the present design Raphael is concerned with establishing the general construction of the composition, where the three figures form a monumental triangle animated by the Leonardesque turn of the Virgin's torso and the arrested movement of the Christ Child, who reaches forward to seize the cross held by the Infant Baptist. Only the staff of the cross, a prominent accent in the painting, is visible in the present design. At the top of the sheet appear studies of the Virgin's drapery and the Infant Baptist's right arm. The young Raphael has used red chalk with admirable ease to suggest the subtle contrasts of light and shade that model the figures; the drawing is one of the earliest examples of the artist's use of this drawing medium.

Raphael's pen study of a nude male figure on the verso of the sheet is strikingly different in intention and treatment from the red chalk drawing on the recto. The male figure has been drawn with a forceful pen line and sharp anatomical observation from a model in the studio, while the red chalk drawing, certainly not drawn from life, is a composition sketch where the artist is concerned with overall construction and lighting of a pictorial scheme and not with exact detail. The nude male figure, with head hanging limply forward and arms raised behind his back by cords that are hardly indicated, may well be a study for the figure of one of the thieves on the cross. Several drawings, datable on stylistic grounds to about the same time as the Metropolitan's sheet, testify that Raphael in his Florentine period had investigated solutions for a representation of the Descent from the Cross, and he may have intended to include the crucified thieves in the scene. On the verso of a sheet in the Albertina, bearing a study for one of the predella panels for the 1507 Borghese Gallery *Entombment of Christ*, is a pen design for a Descent from the Cross (Fischel, no. 182). Stylistically related to this Vienna sheet is a pen drawing in the Louvre (Fischel, no. 183) of a nude male figure hanging as from a cross; the figure is seen full length, but clearly derives from the male nude in the present drawing. The somewhat dry and schematic draughtsmanship of the Paris sketch suggests that it is not a study from life, but one worked up from the example of the Metropolitan's drawing or a similar study after a model.

PROVENANCE: Lambert ten Kate Hermansz., Amsterdam; Ten Kate sale, Amsterdam, June 16, 1732, portfolio H, no. 31; Antoine Rutgers, Amsterdam; Rutgers sale, Amsterdam, December 1, 1778, no. 268; Cornelis Ploos van Amstel (Lugt 2034); Ploos van Amstel sale, Amsterdam, March 3, 1800, portfolio EEE, no. 3; George Hibbert, London; Hibbert sale, London, Christie's, June 12, 1833, no. 169; Samuel Rogers, London; Rogers sale, London, Christie's, beginning April 28, 1856, no. 951; T. Birchall;

Richard Rainshaw Rothwell; J. W. Rothwell; sale, London, Sotheby's, March 11, 1964, no. 150, bought by the Metropolitan Museum.

BIBLIOGRAPHY: Bernard Picart, *Impostures innocentes ou recueil d'estampes d'après divers peintres illustres, tel que Rafael, le Guide, Carlo Maratti, le Poussin, Rembrandt, etc.*, Amsterdam, 1734, pl. 5 (recto engraved in reverse); Passavant, *Raphaël et son père*, II, p. 496, no. 454; Rudolph Weigel, *Die Werke der Maler in ihren Handzeichnungen*, Leipzig, 1865, p. 546, no. 6497; J. A. Crowe and G. B. Cavalcaselle, *Raphael. His Life and Works*, I, London, 1882, p. 264; Fischel, p. 140, n. 2; Parker, *Ashmolean Catalogue*, II, p. 267; J. Bean, "A Rediscovered Drawing by Raphael," *Metropolitan Museum of Art Bulletin*, Summer 1964, pp. 1–10, repr. frontispiece (recto), p. 8, cover (verso); Bean, *100 European Drawings*, no. 12, repr.

EXHIBITIONS: Manchester, "Art Treasures Exhibition, Drawings and Sketches of Old Masters," 1857, no. 49.

The Metropolitan Museum of Art
Rogers Fund, 64.47

50 *Male Figure Symbolizing an Earthquake*

Metalpoint, heightened with white, on gray prepared paper. Diameter 4¼ inches (10.8 cm.).

Study for a figure personifying the earthquake that freed St. Paul from prison. *The Liberation of St. Paul* was designed by Raphael as one of the ten scenes from the Acts of the Apostles for tapestries intended to ornament the lower walls of the Sistine Chapel. Raphael received the first payment for this commission in June 1515; the last was made on December 20 of the following year. The completed cartoons were dispatched to Brussels, where the tapestries were woven. Full-scale cartoons for seven of the tapestries are now in the Victoria and Albert Museum in London, but the *Liberation of St. Paul* is one of the tapestries of which the preparatory cartoon has disappeared. In the tapestry itself, preserved in the Vatican, the figure of the earthquake god appears in reverse in the lower part of the composition, shaking the rocky foundations of the prison in which St. Paul is incarcerated. This rare record of Raphael's preparations for the Vatican tapestries is very close in style and technique to a metalpoint drawing in the Devonshire Collection that is a study for the figure of St. Paul in the tapestry representing the *Sacrifice at Lystra* (repr. *Old Master Drawings from Chatsworth. A Loan Exhibition . . . Circulated by the Smithsonian Institu-*

tion, 1962–1963, no. 58). Passavant (*Raphaël et son père*, II, p. 204) confused a larger pen and wash drawing of the earthquake figure, formerly in the Roscoe Collection, with the present drawing. The present whereabouts of the Roscoe study is unknown.

PROVENANCE: Jonathan Richardson Senior (Lugt 2183); Sir Joshua Reynolds (Lugt 2364).

BIBLIOGRAPHY: Charles Rogers, *A Collection of Prints in Imitation of Drawings*, I, London, 1778, p. 46; Georg Kauffmann, "Zu Raffaels Teppich Paulus im Gefängnis," *Münchner Jahrbuch der Bildenden Kunst*, XV, 1964, pp. 123–130, fig. 3.

EXHIBITIONS: Bloomington, Scholz Exhibition, 1958, no. 18, repr.; Hamburg, Scholz Exhibition, 1963, no. 128, pl. 24; New Haven, Scholz Exhibition, 1964, no. 46, repr. back cover.

Janos Scholz

Giovanni Antonio da Pordenone

Pordenone 1484–Ferrara 1539

51 *The Crucifixion*

Red chalk. 7¹/₁₆ × 8 inches (17.8 × 20.4 cm.). Lined. The sheet has been variously cut at the right, and the rectangular piece with the horseman appears to have been an insertion by the artist to incorporate changes in the composition.

The asymmetrical scheme of Pordenone's fresco of the *Crucifixion* (1520) for the cathedral at Cremona had already been established in this early compositional sketch, although the artist had not yet indicated the positions of the crosses of the two thieves. In the painting they rise just behind the mounted standard bearer on the left, and slightly to the right and back of the horseman on the right. Detail studies of the latter horseman exist in the Louvre and Albertina; a study of the figure of a running boy (not indicated in the present sketch) is in the Koenigs Collection at the Museum Boymans–van Beuningen (Inv. I, 37), Rotterdam.

It is typical of Fairfax Murray's astuteness that he properly attributed this drawing to Pordenone as early as 1912.

PROVENANCE: Jonathan Richardson Senior (Lugt 2183); Sir John Charles Robinson; Sale of a Well-known Amateur [Sir John Charles Robinson], London, Christie's,

May 12, 1902, no. 264 (as Sebastiano del Piombo); Charles Fairfax Murray; purchased by J. Pierpont Morgan in London, 1910.

BIBLIOGRAPHY: Berenson, 1903, p. 233, n. 1, no. 2490 (as Sebastiano del Piombo); Fairfax Murray, IV, no. 69, repr.; K. Schwarzweller, "G. A. da Pordenone," Ph.D. Thesis, Göttingen, 1935, p. 133; E. Tietze-Conrat, "Zwei venezianische Zeichnungen der Albertina," *Die Graphischen Künste*, n.s. II, 1937, p. 86; Berenson, 1938, p. 241, n. 1, no. 2490, fig. 748 (as Sebastiano del Piombo); Giuseppe Fiocco, *Giovanni Antonio Pordenone*, Padua, 1943, pp. 84, 88, 111, 126, pl. 94; Rodolfo Pallucchini, *Sebastian Viniziano (fra Sebastiano del Piombo)*, Milan, 1944, pp. 82, 192; Tietze, *Venetian Drawings*, no. 1340, pl. XCII; Berenson, 1961, no. 2490 B (as Sebastiano del Piombo); Philip Pouncey, review of Bernard Berenson, *I Disegni dei pittori fiorentini*, in *Master Drawings*, II, 1964, p. 291.

The Pierpont Morgan Library
No. IV, 69

52 *St. Christopher*

Pen and brown ink, brown wash, heightened with white, on blue paper. Squared vertically and horizontally in black chalk, diagonally in red chalk. A number of spots of brown wash on the paper. 14¼ × 9¾ inches (36.2 × 24.8 cm.). Lined.

In 1528 Pordenone was comissioned to decorate the choir of the church of S. Rocco in Venice. Little, unfortunately, remains of the frescoes, destroyed or repainted beyond recognition in the eighteenth century, but two panels with splendid figures of St. Christopher and St. Martin of Tours have survived (repr. Venturi, IX, Part 3, figs. 464, 465). Now hanging on the left wall of the church, these panels may have served originally as doors to a cupboard for ecclesiastical silver. The present drawing is an elaborate squared study for the figure of St. Christopher. The diagonal grid of squaring, superimposed on the more conventional vertical-horizontal pattern, reveals Pordenone's concern for the dramatic proto-baroque diagonal stance of the giant figure; and the importance of the white gouache highlights in the modeling of the muscular figure announces the strong contrasts of light and shade in the panel. An old copy of the drawing, once in the collection of Baron Vivant-Denon and reproduced in his *Monuments des arts du dessin*, Paris, 1829, is now in the Crocker Gallery at Sacramento (Tietze, *Venetian Drawings*, no. A 1350). At Chantilly there is a red chalk study by Pordenone for the figure of St. Martin dividing his cloak in the pendant S. Rocco panel (repr. Giuseppe Fiocco, *Giovanni Antonio Pordenone*, Padua, 1943, pl. 133).

PROVENANCE: John Skippe; his descendants, the Martin family, including Mrs. A. D. Rayner-Wood; Edward Holland Martin; Skippe sale, London, Christie's, November 20–21, 1958, no. 161; purchased by the Metropolitan Museum in London, 1960.

BIBLIOGRAPHY: Tietze, *Venetian Drawings*, no. 1334, pl. XCIV, 4; J. Bean, *Metropolitan Museum of Art Bulletin*, January 1962, repr. p. 161, fig. 4; Bean, *100 European Drawings*, no. 13, repr.

The Metropolitan Museum of Art
The Elisha Whittelsey Collection, 60.135

53 *The Conversion of St. Paul*

Pen and brown ink, brown wash, heightened with white, on gray-green paper. 10¾ × 16⅛ inches (27.2 × 41 cm.). Lined. Somewhat abraded, various small losses and stains.

Pordenone's fame, according to Vasari, was established by his paintings of the *Assumption* and the *Conversion of St. Paul*, decorating the wings of the organ of the cathedral at Spilimbergo near Udine, a commission of 1524. Although the elaborate composition of the powerful New York drawing has no connection with the Spilimbergo *St. Paul*, it is quite possible that it was a preparation for another, probably later, painting of the subject. In support of this hypothesis, the Tietzes called attention to two illustrations in the inventory of the Vendramin Collection that depict details of the Morgan composition as separate pictures, the horse and running man at the left and the horseman at the right (Tancred Borenius, *The Picture Gallery of Andrea Vendramin*, London, 1923, pls. 28 and 32). A red chalk drawing at Windsor (Popham-Wilde, *Italian Drawings at Windsor*, no. 749), of unknown authorship but catalogued for convenience as "attributed to Pordenone," also shows the horseman on the right in almost identical form, as well as the foremost horseman in the center and the two figures behind St. Paul.

PROVENANCE: Everhard Jabach (according to Sir John Charles Robinson's inscription on the mount); William Esdaile (Lugt 2617); Thomas Thane (according to Robin-son inscription); John William Spread; Spread sale, London, Christie's, April 27–29, 1898, no. 123; Sir John Charles Robinson (Lugt 1433); Charles Fairfax Murray; purchased by J. Pierpont Morgan in London, 1910.

BIBLIOGRAPHY: Fairfax Murray, I, no. 70, repr.; Lili Fröhlich-Bum, "Beiträge zum Werke des Giovanni Antonio Pordenone," *Münchner Jahrbuch der Bildenden Kunst*, 1925, n. s. II, pp. 85, 86; Giuseppe Fiocco, *Giovanni Antonio Pordenone*, Padua, 1943, pp. 86, 90, 154, pl. 180; Tietze, *Venetian Drawings*, no. 1341; Popham-Wilde, *Italian Drawings at Windsor*, p. 302, under no. 749.

The Pierpont Morgan Library
No. I, 70

Girolamo Romani, called Romanino

Brescia about 1485–Brescia 1559/1561

54 *Concert Champêtre*

Pen and brown ink, brown wash, over black chalk. Occasional extraneous faint smudges of red chalk. 11½ × 16⅜ inches (29.3 × 41 cm.). Two repaired tears at right center; loss at right center, upper edge.

Inscribed in pencil at lower right, *Giorgione*.

The Lehman composition, showing a sylvan string quartet with a fifth figure looking on, is the most elaborate of three Romanino drawings of musical groups featuring a faun, although they do not develop precisely the same idea and are in different media. The sheet of studies of a lute player in the Uffizi is in pen (repr. *Mostra di strumenti musicali in disegni degli Uffizi*, Florence, 1952, fig. 12); the *Pastoral Concert* in the collection of Janos Scholz is in red chalk (repr. Ferrari, *Romanino*, p. 17, fig. b). It is logical to associate these drawings with Romanino's two lunettes of concert groups among the frescoes decorating the loggia of the Castello del Buonconsiglio at Trento (1531–1532), despite the fact that there is no direct connection between any of the drawings and the painted compositions. The latter are devoid of the poetic fantasy of the drawings, which are lightly Giorgionesque in mood.

The drawing passed under the name of Pordenone at the Grassi sale in 1924 and has since on occasion figured under that name. The convincing ascription to Romanino was made at the time of the exhibition of the Lehman Collection in Paris.

PROVENANCE: Luigi Grassi (Lugt S. 1171b); sale, under the initials G. L. [Grassi], London, Sotheby's, May 13, 1924, no. 107, repr.

EXHIBITIONS: Paris, Lehman Collection, 1957, no. 124; Cincinnati, Lehman Collection, 1959, no. 216, repr.

Robert Lehman

55 *Back View of a Soldier with a Plumed Hat and Sketch of Another Soldier*

Red chalk. 11⅜ × 7⅞ inches (28.8 × 20.1 cm.).

Inscribed in red chalk at lower center, *Hieronimo Romanino da Bressa.*

In the catalogue of the Venice exhibition of drawings from the Scholz Collection, Muraro suggested that these studies of soldiers are related to Romanino's four scenes of the Passion painted in fresco in the nave of the cathedral at Cremona. Indeed, very similar soldiers in German costumes with plumed hats are conspicuous figures in these compositions datable 1519–1520 (repr. Ferrari, pls. 28–36). However, Florence Kossoff has quite recently proposed that the drawing is more likely to be a preparatory study for a warrior in one of the battle scenes at the Castle of Malpagna, attributed by her and Morassi to Romanino. The firm, mature style of the draughtsmanship corresponds well with the later date of these frescoes. The old inscription on the sheet attributing the drawing to Romanino is certainly correct; the irregular flickering red chalk line and the energetic physical type sketched here are typical of the artist.

BIBLIOGRAPHY: Ferrari, *Romanino*, opposite pl. 30; Florence Kossoff, "A New Book on Romanino," *Burlington Magazine*, CV, 1963, p. 77.

EXHIBITIONS: Oakland, Scholz Exhibition, 1956, no. 75; Venice, Scholz Exhibition, 1957, no. 14, repr.; Bloomington, Scholz Exhibition, 1958, no. 30, repr.; Oakland, Scholz Exhibition, 1959, no. 59; Hamburg, Scholz Exhibition, 1963, no. 19, pl. 136; Brescia, "Mostra di Girolamo Romanino," 1965, no. 123, pl. 209.

Janos Scholz

56 *Nude Male Figure*

Brush and brown wash, over slight traces of black chalk. 11⁹⁄₁₆ × 6⁹⁄₁₆ inches (29.4 × 16.7 cm.). Repairs at upper, lower, and right margins. Lined.

Inscribed in pen and brown ink at upper right corner, *Gerolamo Romanino Prattico / Pittore Bresciano.* A long inscription in pen and brown ink at upper right has been erased and is now illegible.

This tensely posed figure is modeled entirely with the point of brush, in a technique that is strikingly similar to the feathery brushwork in Romanino's fresco painting. Florence Kossoff has suggested that the figure may be a preparatory study for the Adam in the scene representing Christ in Limbo, part of Romanino's fresco cycle in S. Maria della Neve at Pisogne near Brescia (repr. Ferrari, *Romanino*, pl. 79). If the drawing is not actually connected with the fresco, it may well date from the same time, about 1534.

PROVENANCE: Purchased by the Metropolitan Museum in London, 1961.

BIBLIOGRAPHY: Antonio Morassi, "Alcuni disegni inediti del Romanino," *Festschrift Karl M. Swoboda*, Vienna, 1959, p. 190, fig. 39; J. Bean, *Metropolitan Museum of Art Bulletin*, January 1962, repr. p. 163, fig. 6; Creighton Gilbert, "Una Monografia sul Romanino," *Arte Veneta*, XVI, 1962, p. 201, fig. 232; Florence Kossoff, "A New Book on Romanino," *Burlington Magazine*, CV, 1963, p. 77, fig. 52.

The Metropolitan Museum of Art
Rogers Fund, 61.123.3

Sebastiano del Piombo

Venice 1485–Rome 1547

57 *Seated Sibyl*

Red chalk on light brown paper. 9⅞ × 10⁷⁄₁₆ inches (24.4 × 26.5 cm.). All four corners replaced. Partially lined.

Inscribed in pen and brown ink at upper left, *79.*

Verso: Study in pen and brown ink of a horse's head.

This study of a seated sibyl listening to the whispered counsel of a ghostly genius who appears behind her was first identified as the work of Sebastiano del Piombo by Philip Pouncey. The drawing cannot be connected with any extant painted work by the artist, but it is not difficult to imagine this massive, hieratic figure watching over some sacred scene represented in a great fresco or panel painting. The heavy drapery, treated in broad sculptural folds, the powerful, noble profile of the sibyl, the curious foreshortening of her right shoulder, and the deliberate exaggeration of the size of her hands are all eminently typical of Sebastiano's mature style. The figure is certainly inspired by the sibyls in the Sistine Chapel, and the monumental sculptural style is also drawn directly from Michelangelo. Sebastiano's own Venetian pictorial tendencies are apparent in one passage of the drawing, where the heavily accentuated profile of the sibyl is silhouetted against the shimmering suggestion of the head of the genius.

PROVENANCE: Hugh N. Squire, London; purchased by the Metropolitan Museum in London, 1962.

BIBLIOGRAPHY: J. Bean, *Metropolitan Museum of Art Bulletin*, March 1963, pp. 232–233, fig. 6; Bean, *100 European Drawings*, no. 14, repr.

The Metropolitan Museum of Art
Gustavus A. Pfeiffer Fund, 62.120.7

Tiziano Vecellio, called Titian

Pieve di Cadore 1485/1488(?)–Venice 1576

58 *A Group of Trees*

Pen and brown ink on brownish paper. 8%6 × 12%6 inches (21.7 × 31.9 cm.).

Inscribed in darker brown ink at lower margin, *Giorgione.*

The old attribution to Giorgione inscribed on the drawing is misleading, and since Colvin first published it in 1909 as the work of Titian it has generally been accepted as one of the rare examples of his landscape drawing. Von Hadeln hesitatingly placed the drawing in the circle of Titian, but the exceptional quality and power of the draughtsmanship testify convincingly in the favor of Titian's own authorship. The Tietzes have pointed out that the drawing was used in a woodcut after a design by Titian. In this print representing the Sacrifice of Abraham, the first version of which was executed by Ugo da Carpi, the trees and the stump in the right half of the drawing appear in reverse near the lower right margin. What has not been observed before is that in the drawing itself the pen lines are somewhat blurred. This suggests that two ink counterproofs may have been made from the sheet in the course of transferring the outlines of

the trees onto the large design that Titian must have supplied to the printmaker.

PROVENANCE: Charles Sackville Bale; Bale sale, London, Christie's, June 9, 1881, no. 2298 (as Giorgione); Sir James Knowles, London; Knowles sale, London, Christie's, May 27, 1908, no. 181 (as Titian), bought by the Metropolitan Museum.

BIBLIOGRAPHY: Sidney Colvin, *Vasari Society*, first series, V, 1909–1910, no. 9, repr.; Detlev von Hadeln, *Titian's Drawings*, London, 1927, pp. 15–16, 24, pl. 45; Lili Frölich-Bum, "Die Landschaftszeichnungen Tizians," *Belvedere*, VIII, 1929, p. 77; Hans Tietze and E. Tietze-Conrat, "Titian-Studien," *Jahrbuch der Kunsthistorischen Sammlungen in Wien*, n. s., X, 1936, pp. 167, 191, n. 7, fig. 145 (related woodcut fig. 143); Metropolitan Museum, *European Drawings*, I, repr. no. 14; Tietze, *Venetian Drawings*, no. 1943, pl. LXIII, 2; Tietze, *European Master Drawings*, p. 54, no. 27, repr. p. 55; Mongan, *One Hundred Drawings*, p. 48, repr. p. 49; Tietze, *Titian*, p. 404, pl. 47; Bean, *100 European Drawings*, no. 15, repr.

EXHIBITIONS: Toledo, Venetian Painting, 1940, no. 95; Philadelphia, Masterpieces of Drawing, 1950–1951, no. 35, repr.; New York, Pierpont Morgan Library, "Landscape Drawings and Water-Colors, Bruegel to Cézanne," 1953, no. 8.

The Metropolitan Museum of Art
Rogers Fund, 08.227.38

59 *Two Satyrs Holding an Astrolabe in a Landscape*

Pen and brown ink, heightened with white. 8%6 × 5¹⁵⁄16 inches (22.7 × 15.1 cm.). The faces of both satyrs, the leg and right arm of the satyr with his back turned, and the forearm of the satyr looking out have been retouched in part.

Inscribed in pen and brown ink at lower right, *Lovini Milanese.*

The authorship and the subject of this fascinating drawing have provoked a good deal of still inconclusive discussion. An old inscription on the sheet, *Lovini Milanese*, presumably proposes the quite untenable attribution to the Milanese Bernardino Luini. The figure and the landscape style both suggest that the drawing is Venetian and that it dates from the early sixteenth century. The Tietzes claimed it for Titian himself, but though the draughtsmanship and the subject reveal the preponderant influence of the early style of this master, it is far from certain that he is the author of this sheet, although it is exhibited here under his name.

Parker hesitantly proposed an attribution to Domenico Campagnola, Brendel has suggested the name of Dosso Dossi, and Pallucchini has called the drawing a relatively early work of Sebastiano del Piombo, at a period when Titian's influence was predominant in Sebastiano's style. The pen work as well as the physical types do show marked similarities with the early drawings of Sebastiano, but Pallucchini's attribution remains speculative. Various readings of the horoscope inscribed on the astrolabe have been suggested, and Agnes Mongan has discussed the possible astrological significance of the drawing in the catalogue of the Fogg Museum's exhibition of Mr. Baer's drawings.

PROVENANCE: Earls of Pembroke; Pembroke sale, London, Sotheby's, July 5–10, 1917, no. 318 (as Venetian school); Henry Oppenheimer; Oppenheimer sale, London, Christie's, July 10–14, 1936, no. 42 (as Domenico Campagnola).

BIBLIOGRAPHY: Strong, *Wilton House Drawings*, Part VI, repr. no. 54 (as Venetian school); Hans Tietze, *Tizian. Leben und Werk*, Vienna, 1936, I, pp. 156, 239; II, p. 319, pl. 7; H. Tietze and E. Tietze-Conrat, "Tizian-Studien," *Jahrbuch der Kunsthistorischen Sammlungen in Wien*, n. s., X, 1936, p. 169, pl. 149; Rodolfo Pallucchini, *Sebastian Viniziano*, Milan, 1944, p. 80, pl. 85; Tietze, *Venetian Drawings*, no. 1948, pl. LIX (additional references given in this volume); Tietze, *Titian*, pp. 31, 404–405, pl. 7; Otto Brendel, "Borrowings from Ancient Art in Titian," *The Art Bulletin*, XXXVII, 1955, p. 118, fig. 9 (detail).

EXHIBITIONS: Montreal, Five Centuries of Drawings, 1953, no. 51, repr.; Cambridge, Massachusetts, Fogg Art Museum, "Drawings from the Collection of Curtis O. Baer," 1958, no. 1, repr.; Newark, Old Master Drawings, 1960, no. 21, repr.

Curtis O. Baer

Andrea del Sarto

Florence 1486–Florence 1530

60 *Youth Carrying a Sack on His Head*

Black chalk. 10⅜ × 5¼ inches (26.3 × 13.4 cm.). Watermark: anchor (close to Briquet 433). Crease at lower left; pale brown stain at left, and splashes of brown on verso.

Verso: Details of the same figure in red and black chalk.

Like most of Andrea's drawings, the lithe youth gracefully counterbalancing his burdens as he climbs a stair is a study from the model. As was pointed out by Dr. Waagen when he saw the drawing in the collection of Samuel Rogers more than a century ago, it is preparatory for the figure of the serving man at the right in the *Visitation*, one of the later compositions (payment recorded November 1524) in the series of now badly damaged grisaille frescoes in the cloister of the barefooted monks of the Confraternity of St. John the Baptist, in Florence, a project on which Andrea worked at intervals from 1506 until 1526. On the verso, the artist, as was often his practice, studied certain details of the figure more carefully, making first a sketch of the upper part of the figure recording the youth's features and concentrating on the supporting left arm, then an even more specific note of the supple curve of the left hand and wrist as they bent over the sack, and finally a sketch of the sack itself. He utilized these details in the finished fresco, where such passages as the pattern of the rippling sleeve folds and the features conform to the verso sketches rather than to the more generalized forms of the complete figure in which the calibration of movement and equilibrium was his chief concern.

At least one other study for the Visitation fresco has been identified, the red chalk drawing in Dijon (Freedberg, p. 130) for the head and left hand of Zachary.

PROVENANCE: Jonathan Richardson Senior (Lugt 2184); Sir Joshua Reynolds (Lugt 2364); Samuel Rogers (according to Dr. Waagen); E. A. Leatham; sale including Leatham, London, Christie's, June 2, 1902, no. 115; Charles Fairfax Murray; purchased by J. Pierpont Morgan in London, 1910.

BIBLIOGRAPHY: Jonathan Richardson, *An Account of the Statues, Bas-reliefs, Drawings and Pictures in Italy, France, etc.*, London, 1722, p. 83; Dr. Waagen, *Treasures of Art in Great Britain*, II, London, 1854, p. 80; Berenson, 1903, no. 55; Fairfax Murray, I, no. 30, repr.; Fritz Knapp, *Andrea del Sarto*, Leipzig, 1907, p. 135; Berenson, 1938, no. 141 E; Tietze, *European Master Drawings*, no. 25, repr.; Mongan, *One Hundred Drawings*, p. 52, repr.; James Watrous, *The Craft of Old Master Drawings*, Madison, 1957, p. 100; Berenson, 1961, no. 141 E; Sidney Freedberg, *Andrea del Sarto*, Cambridge, Massachusetts, 1963, under no. 60, figs. 93–94; John Shearman, *Andrea del Sarto*, Oxford, 1965, I, p. 150; II, pp. 305 under no. 14, 366.

EXHIBITIONS: New London, Fourth Anniversary Exhibition, 1936, no. 23; Northampton, Smith College, Italian Drawings, 1941, no. 44; Worcester, Fiftieth Anniversary

Exhibition, 1948, no. 34; Cambridge, Massachusetts, Fogg Art Museum, "Seventy Master Drawings," 1948, no. 23; New York, Morgan Library, Fiftieth Anniversary Exhibition, 1957, no. 85, pl. 53; Newark, Old Master Drawings, 1960, no. 11, repr.

The Pierpont Morgan Library
No. I, 30

Domenico Beccafumi

Near Siena 1486(?)–Siena 1551

61 Head of Thrasybulus

Tempera and emulsion; contours incised. 11¼ × 8 inches (28.5 × 20.3 cm.). Losses at corners, break at left center. Lined.

In preparing his paintings and frescoes, Beccafumi frequently followed the practice of making preliminary brush studies in tempera on paper, like this one and Nos. 62 and 63 of the exhibition. The life-size head of the old man is one of thirteen such studies related to the frescoes on the ceiling of the Sala del Concistoro in the Palazzo Pubblico at Siena, painted between 1529 and 1535. It is intended to portray the Greek general and statesman Thrasybulus (died 388 B.C.), one of eight patriotic personages represented in pairs in the corners of the Concistoro vault. The other tempera sketches for the frescoes are in Amsterdam, Cambridge, Massachusetts, London, Princeton, and Wiesbaden, and also in the collection of Mrs. Edward Fowles (the former Mrs. Langton Douglas), of New York.

PROVENANCE: Sir Joseph Hawley; sale, London, Christie's, July 16, 1891, no. 194; Charles Fairfax Murray; purchased by J. Pierpoint Morgan in London, 1910.

BIBLIOGRAPHY: J. Judey, "Beccafumi," Inaugural Dissertation, Albert-Ludwigs-Universität, Freiburg im Breisgau, 1932, no. 225; Agnes Mongan and Paul J. Sachs, *Drawings in the Fogg Museum of Art*, I, Cambridge, Massachusetts, 1950, p. 54; Sanminiatelli, *Burlington Magazine*, 1955, p. 36, fig. 2.

EXHIBITIONS: New York, Columbia Benefit Exhibition, 1959, no. 17, pl. 15.

The Pierpont Morgan Library
No. I, 19B

62 Head of the Good Thief

Tempera and emulsion; contours in part incised. 10 × 8⅛ inches (25.4 × 20.6 cm.). Some breaks and losses. Lined.

This boldly brushed study was used without change for the head of the Good Thief in the *Descent of Christ into Limbo*, the large altarpiece Beccafumi painted for the Marsili Chapel in S. Francesco, Siena, and now in the Accademia di Belle Arti of that city. The head, as Sanminiatelli remarks, bears a curious resemblance to the artist's own features as revealed in the *Self-Portrait* in the Uffizi. The same authority dates the altarpiece about 1535; others have placed it a decade earlier. Two other studies for the painting are found in the Chigi-Saraceni Collection and in the Uffizi.

PROVENANCE: Sir Joseph Hawley; sale, London, Christie's, July 16, 1891, no. 194; Charles Fairfax Murray; purchased by J. Pierpont Morgan in London, 1910.

BIBLIOGRAPHY: J. Judey, "Beccafumi," Inaugural Dissertation, Albert-Ludwigs-Universität, Freiburg im Breisgau, 1932, no. 226; Sanminiatelli, *Burlington Magazine*, 1955, p. 37.

EXHIBITIONS: Hartford, Morgan Treasures, 1960, no. 67.

The Pierpont Morgan Library
No. I, 19A

63 St. Matthew

Tempera and emulsion. 15⅝ × 8⅝ inches (39.8 × 22 cm.).

The powerful figure of the Evangelist crowding the confines of the niche is a study for the *St. Matthew* painted in Siena in 1538 but destined for the choir of the cathedral at Pisa. The artist made a number of changes between the monochrome study and the painting, where he altered the position of the arms and hands, turned the Evangelist's head to the right, and reversed the direction of the light. In connection with these rather extensive revisions, it is interesting to note that the companion *St. Mark*, also owned by Mrs. Fowles, was apparently followed by the pen sketch now in the Cabinet des Dessins at the Louvre (Inv. 252), since the Louvre version is somewhat closer to the finished painting (*Choix de dessins de maîtres florentins et siennois*, Cabinet des Dessins, 1955, no. 67). In contrast to this procedure, Nos. 61–62 of the exhibition, which show incising of the contours, served without alteration as the cartoons for the finished works.

PROVENANCE: Henry S. Reitlinger; Reitlinger sale, London, Sotheby's, December 9, 1954, no. 24.

BIBLIOGRAPHY: Sanminiatelli, *Burlington Magazine*, 1955, p. 35, n. 5.

Mrs. Edward Fowles

64 *Gaius Mucius Scaevola Holding His Hand in the Fire*

Red chalk. 11⅝ × 8¹³⁄₁₆ inches (29.6 × 22.4 cm.). Watermark: anvil in a circle (Briquet 5964).

Inscribed on verso in an old hand in pen and brown ink, *Domenico Beccafumo detto Meccarino / 2.4.*

Gaius Mucius Scaevola was the legendary Roman who, when he was taken prisoner after his failure to slay Lars Porsenna, demonstrated his courage in the face of death by thrusting his right hand into the fire; he was henceforth known as Scaevola or "left-handed." One might, therefore, have expected to find him among the company of noble heroes portrayed in the ceiling frescoes of the Sala del Concistoro of the Palazzo Pubblico at Siena, but he is not there despite his striking resemblance to such figures as Servilius Ahala. On the other hand, the polished detail of the drawing may indicate that Beccafumi had a print in view. A pen drawing, also in the Morgan Library, shows on recto and verso two preliminary sketches for the finished red chalk composition.

PROVENANCE: Sir Peter Lely (Lugt 2092); J. Isaacs; Isaacs sale, London, Sotheby's, February 27, 1964, no. 124; purchased by the Pierpont Morgan Library in London, 1964.

The Pierpont Morgan Library
Gift of the Fellows, 1964.7

Antonio Allegri, called Correggio

Correggio 1489/1494–Correggio 1534

65 *Head of a Woman Crying Out*

Charcoal, in some passages blended with white chalk, and accents in brush and black oil pigment. The sheet, made up of two pieces of paper pasted together, has irregular margins. At widest point 12⅝ × 8⅞ inches (32.2 × 22.4 cm.). Lined.

The unquestionable correspondence of this cartoon fragment with the head of the lamenting Mary at the upper right in *Christ's Entombment*, one of the ruined fresco roundels in the portico of S. Andrea at Mantua, was A. E. Popham's remarkable discovery. The frescoes have been traditionally attributed to Correggio since the early seventeenth century. The only other Correggio cartoon known is the black chalk head of an angel at the École des Beaux-Arts, Paris (Popham, no. 71), also a fragment.

Like the sketches for Fontanellato by Parmigianino (No. 88 of the exhibition), this drawing passed through the Haym and Spencer collections and may possibly also have come from the Arundel Collection.

PROVENANCE: N. F. Haym (Lugt 1970); The Earls Spencer (Lugt 1530); Charles Fairfax Murray; purchased by J. Pierpont Morgan in London, 1910.

BIBLIOGRAPHY: Fairfax Murray, IV, no. 30, repr.; K. T. Parker, *North Italian Drawings of the Quattrocento*, London, 1927, no. 27, pl. 27; Tietze, *European Master Drawings*, no. 15, repr.; Popham, *Correggio's Drawings*, pp. 13, 78, 149, no. 1, pl. 2; Stefano Bottari, *Correggio*, Milan, 1961, p. 10; Moskowitz, ed., *Great Drawings*, I, no. 265, repr.

EXHIBITIONS: New York, Columbia Benefit Exhibition, 1959, no. 14, pl. 14; Hartford, Morgan Treasures, 1960, no. 68.

The Pierpont Morgan Library
No. IV, 30

66 *The Adoration of the Magi*

Red chalk heightened with white. 11½ × 7¾ inches (29.2 × 19.7 cm.).

An early drawing by Correggio, datable toward the end of the second decade of the sixteenth century. Red chalk and white highlights are used to create the soft luminosity that also characterizes Correggio's paintings of this same period. Popham has suggested that the drawing may be a stage of the artist's preparation for the *Adoration of the Magi*, now in the Brera in Milan (repr. Popham, p. 18, fig. 3) and has drawn attention to the Northern influences apparent in both the drawing and the picture—echoes of Hugo van der Goes in composition and of Dürer in several details. The prototype of the rather awkwardly drawn horse may be Mercury's steed in the *Parnassus* of Mantegna, now in the Louvre. Doubts about Correggio's authorship of this drawing have occasionally been emitted: Ricci, who presumably knew the drawing only through a reproduction, proposed an untenable attribution to Bertoia; Mrs. Heaton-Sessions questioned the drawing without suggesting an alternative solution. Popham, however, has insisted on the authenticity of the drawing. The way in which chalk and white lights are used, the facial notations, and the treatment of the drapery all proclaim this drawing to be an original by Correggio, and to be an early work in which some of the most striking pictorial elements of his mature style are already present.

PROVENANCE: Sir Peter Lely (Lugt 2092); Earls of Pembroke; Pembroke sale, London, Sotheby's, July 5–10, 1917, no. 464, bought by the Metropolitan Museum.

BIBLIOGRAPHY: Strong, *Wilton House Drawings*, Part II, repr. no. 14; Sturge Moore, *Correggio*, pp. 215, 262; Ricci, *Correggio*, p. 184; Metropolitan Museum, *European Drawings*, I, repr. no. 20; Heaton-Sessions, *Art Bulletin*, 1954, pp. 224–225, fig. 5; Popham, *Correggio's Drawings*, pp. 10, 50, 150, no. 5, pl. VI; Bean, *100 European Drawings*, no. 16, repr.

*The Metropolitan Museum of Art
Hewitt Fund, 19.76.10*

67 Study of a Male Figure, Nude to the Waist, and of a Putto

Red chalk, pen and brown ink. 4⅟₁₆ × 3¼ inches (10.3 × 8.2 cm.). Repairs at upper left and lower right corners.

Study for one of the Apostles in the frescoed cupola of S. Giovanni Evangelista in Parma, a commission undertaken by Correggio about 1520. Though the figure does not exactly correspond with any one of the Apostles, the twisted pose of the half-nude torso leaning forward on a cloud, the presence of the putto below, and the style of the drawing all suggest the connection with the cupola of S. Giovanni Evangelista. The sketches for volutes of foliage below are no doubt related to the decoration of the narrow band running around the bottom of the dome, where symbols of the Evangelists confront each other against a background of foliage. A tiny red chalk study for another Apostle,

now in the British Museum, is stylistically very similar to the present drawing, which has only recently reappeared. The London drawing, which Popham connects with the S. Giovanni Evangelista frescoes, also belonged to Lely and Reynolds (Popham, no. 15, pl. XVIIa).

PROVENANCE: Sir Peter Lely (Lugt 2092); Sir Joshua Reynolds (Lugt 2364); private collection, Bath.

BIBLIOGRAPHY: Walter Vitzthum, "Drawings from the Scholz Collection in Germany," *Master Drawings*, I, 1963, no. 4, p. 58, fig. 1.

EXHIBITIONS: Hamburg, Scholz Exhibition, 1963, no. 41, pl. 20.

Janos Scholz

68 The Annunciation

Pen and black ink, gray wash, extensively heightened with white, on red washed paper; squared in red chalk. 3¾ × 6¹³⁄₁₆ inches (9.5 × 17.3 cm.).

In this small brush drawing Correggio suggests with almost magical ease and authority the pictorial effect of the fresco for which it is a study. The drawing, a miniature *modello*, must represent one of the last stages in the artist's preparation for the lunette painted for the church of the Annunziata at Capo di Ponte in Parma, now exhibited in a much-damaged state in the gallery of that city (repr. Popham, pl. LVb). The fresco and the present drawing are dated about 1522–1524 by Popham, who compares them to Correggio's contemporary work in S. Giovanni Evangelista in Parma. Several of the artist's preparatory drawings for this latter enterprise display the same vigorous and summary use of thick white highlights to indicate modeling in light and shade.

PROVENANCE: Earls of Pembroke; Pembroke sale, London, Sotheby's, July 5–10, 1917, no. 465, bought by the Metropolitan Museum.

BIBLIOGRAPHY: Strong, *Wilton House Drawings*, Part III, repr. no. 25; Sturge Moore, *Correggio*, pp. 121, 217, repr. opposite p. 242; Bryson Burroughs, "Drawings from the Pembroke Collection," *Metropolitan Museum of Art Bulletin*, June 1919, p. 137, repr. p. 136; Ricci, *Correggio*, p. 167, pl. CCLIIb; Metropolitan Museum, *European Drawings*, I, repr. no. 19; Heaton-Sessions, *Art Bulletin*, 1954, p. 224, fig. I; Popham, *Correggio's Drawings*, pp. 63, 159, no.

49, pl. lva; Moskowitz, ed., *Great Drawings*, I, no. 264, repr.; Bean, *100 European Drawings*, no. 18, repr.

The Metropolitan Museum of Art
Hewitt Fund, 19.76.9

69 *Design for the Decoration of a Pilaster*

Red chalk on beige paper. 12¾ × 8³⁄₁₆ inches (32.3 × 20.8 cm.). Watermark: variant of Briquet 3086.

Inscribed in pen and brown ink in lower margin, *Correggio*.

Verso: Faint red chalk studies for the decoration of a pilaster with a putto holding a quiver.

Building up from a tortoise placed on a double volute, the draughtsman has constructed a twisting column that works up through vase, caduceus, helmet, and scabbard to a terminal cornucopia, supported along the way by putti, birds, and a satyr. Popham suggests that in spite of its entirely secular components, this lively ornament construction may have been designed by Correggio for the painted decoration of the pilasters in the nave of S. Giovanni Evangelista, Parma. The artist's overall commission for work in this church included the decoration of these pilasters, which were finally all ornamented with a standardized painted candelabrum. Attributed in an old inscription on the drawing itself to Correggio, and published as his by Strong, the drawing in recent years has been assigned to a number of artists, all influenced by Correggio. Venturi gave it to Bernardino Gatti, the Tietzes to Pordenone, Mrs. Heaton-Sessions to Pomponio Allegri. Popham has both prudently and convincingly returned it to Correggio himself, pointing out that it is entirely characteristic of the artist's draughtsmanship about the period of his activity in S. Giovanni Evangelista.

PROVENANCE: Sir Peter Lely (Lugt 2092); Earls of Pembroke; Pembroke sale, London, Sotheby's, July 5–10, 1917, no. 409, bought by the Metropolitan Museum.

BIBLIOGRAPHY: Strong, *Wilton House Drawings*, Part V, repr. no. 47; Adolfo Venturi, "Studii sul Correggio," *L'Arte*, V, 1902, pp. 353–354; Sturge Moore, *Correggio*, p. 265; Ricci, *Correggio*, p. 185; Tietze, *Venetian Drawings*, no. 1360; Heaton-Sessions, *Art Bulletin*, 1954, pp. 225–226, fig. 6; Popham, *Correggio's Drawings*, pp. 62, 116, 159, no. 47, pl. liii; Bean, *100 European Drawings*, no. 17, repr.

The Metropolitan Museum of Art
Hewitt Fund, 19.76.12

70 *Allegory of Virtue*

Pen and brown ink, brown wash, over traces of black chalk. 6¼ × 6⅛ inches (15.9 × 15.6 cm.). Vertical tear at lower margin; repairs at all margins.

Inscribed on verso in pen and brown ink, *Correggio | an allegory of heroic virtue — first | thought for the fresco in the Louvre | Sir T. Lawrence*.

Study for an allegorical composition painted in tempera by Correggio in the last four years of his life, between 1530 and 1534, for the *Studio* of Isabella d'Este in the Castello at Mantua. Correggio's two canvases representing allegories of Virtue and Vice originally flanked the doorway of the *Studio*; they are now in the Louvre. In the picture Minerva, holding her helmet, is seated at center, and at the left a seated female figure bears attributes that identify her as a composite allegorical figure symbolizing all four cardinal virtues: Justice, Prudence, Temperance, and Fortitude. In the present drawing the arrangement is reversed, and as Popham points out, numerous variants indicate that the drawing represents an early stage of Correggio's planning for the tempera painting. The Louvre possesses a double-faced preparatory sketch for the *Allegory of Virtue* (Popham, p. 167, no. 89, pls. ciia and ciib). On the recto of the sheet the grouping of the two principal figures corresponds roughly with the final solution, but the two figures on the verso face to the left as in the present drawing, and Popham suggests that it may be an elaboration, perhaps basically a tracing, of the verso of the Louvre sheet.

PROVENANCE: Count Bianconi (according to Lawrence Gallery catalogue); Sir Thomas Lawrence; Samuel Woodburn; Woodburn sale, London, Christie's, July 12, 1887, no. 288; R. P. Roupell (Lugt 2234); Roupell sale, London, Christie's, July 12, 1887, no. 761; J. P. Heseltine (Lugt 1507); Henry Oppenheimer; Oppenheimer sale, London, Christie's, July 10, 1936, no. 121; Wilhelm Suida, New York.

BIBLIOGRAPHY: *The Lawrence Gallery. Fourth Exhibition*, p. 22, no. 86; Popham, *Correggio's Drawings*, pp. 99, 141, 167, no. 90, pl. civ.

EXHIBITIONS: Columbus, Ohio, Columbus Gallery of Fine Arts, "Sir Thomas Lawrence as Painter and Collector," 1955, no. 45.

Robert and Bertina Suida Manning

Polidoro Caldara, called Polidoro da Caravaggio

Caravaggio 1490/1500–Messina 1543 (?)

71 *A Scene of Judgment*

Pen and brown ink, brown wash, heightened with white, over black chalk. 6½ × 9⅛ inches (16.4 × 23.1 cm.). Lined.

An unidentified scene, probably from Roman legend or history, possibly intended for the grisaille decoration of a house façade, the kind of painting that was a specialty of the artist. The drawing presumably was made before Polidoro fled to Naples following the sack of Rome in 1527.

The drawing carries only the collector's mark of Comte Nils Barck, but on the mount there is a penciled notation of the collections of "Crozat, De Tessin, Queen of Sweden (Ulrica), Count de Steenbock, Count de Barck." This inscription may have been copied from an old mount or from the back of the drawing, which is now lined, as Comte Barck apparently on occasion did so inscribe his drawings (cf. Lugt S. 3006c). The drawing seemingly made its way through this long sequence of famous collectors under the correct attribution to Polidoro.

PROVENANCE: Comte Nils Barck (Lugt 1959); Charles Fairfax Murray; purchased by J. Pierpont Morgan in London, 1910.

BIBLIOGRAPHY: Fairfax Murray, I, no. 20, repr.

The Pierpont Morgan Library
No. I, 20

72 *The Virgin and Child Surrounded by Worshipers*

Pen and brown ink, brown wash, heightened with white, on brown washed paper. 8⅛16 × 11³⁄16 inches (20.4 × 28.4 cm.). Several repaired tears at lower margin; upper margin torn irregularly.

Inscribed indistinctly in pen and brown ink at lower left corner, *Polidoro* (?).

This curious composition with a crowd of worshipers pressing toward the Virgin and Child, as figures clinging to trees watch from above, presumably does not represent an Adoration of the Magi, because the principal bearded worshipers do not have royal attributes, and the Christ Child seems to be already several years of age. The figures clinging to trees occur in Polidoro's *Way to Calvary*, a late picture painted for Messina and now at Capodimonte in Naples; the style of the drawing also suggests a fairly late date in Polidoro's career. An old copy of the drawing, in which the spectators clinging to trees have been omitted, is in the Pierpont Morgan Library (repr. Fairfax Murray, IV, no. 18).

Robert and Bertina Suida Manning

73 *Studies for an Altarpiece with the Virgin Enthroned, Attended by Four Saints*

Pen and brown ink. 7⅞ × 11⁹⁄16 inches (20 × 29.4 cm.). The number 27 is imprinted in black ink at lower right of verso. Inscribed in pencil at upper right corner, *P. Veronese. 38.*

Verso: Figure studies in pen and brown ink.

The modern inscription on the recto of this double-faced sheet attributing the drawing to *P. Veronese* is erroneous; the frenzied but highly intelligent pen work is typical of the late style of Polidoro da Caravaggio. Other drawings related to the composition dominated by the enthroned Madonna are known. A study for two of the standing saints, once in Mariette's collection, is now the property of Philip Pouncey in London, and Hugh N. Squire of Orford, Suffolk, possesses a study for the whole group. Pouncey has identified a further study for the group in the Albertina (Wickhoff, *Albertina*, p. CLXXXII, S.R. 22, as Traini). The sketches on the verso of the present sheet cannot be connected with specific compositions known to have been painted by Polidoro but, like the drawing on the recto, they are quite close in style to pen drawings in the British Museum that are very probably studies for a Transfiguration painted for a church in Messina in the last years of the artist's life (the drawings repr. Philip Pouncey and J. A. Gere, *Italian Drawings . . . in the British Museum. Raphael and His Circle*, London, 1962, nos. 217, 218, pls. 188–191).

PROVENANCE: Ferruccio Asta (Lugt 116a).

Walter C. Baker

Michelangelo Anselmi

Lucca 1491–Parma 1555/1556

74 *The Young David Playing the Harp*

Black chalk, gray wash, heightened with white, on blue paper; squared in pen and brown ink. 15⅜ × 5⁷⁄₁₆ inches (38.6 × 14.1 cm.). Lined.

Study for the figure of David painted in monochrome by Anselmi on the entrance arch of the western apse of S. Maria della Steccata in Parma (repr. Augusta Ghidiglia Quintavalle, *Michelangelo Anselmi*, Parma, 1960, fig. 155). The placement of the figure, seated in a niche rounded at top and bottom, is directly inspired by and in imitation of motifs in Parmigianino's unfinished decoration in the vault of the eastern apse of the Steccata (see No. 94 of the exhibition). Anselmi was one of the artists commissioned to continue the decoration of the church after Parmigianino's disgrace and death. Though his formal dependence on Parmigianino's example is evident in this study, his style as a draughtsman is here strikingly different, in its soft pictorial chiaroscuro, from that of Parmigianino.

PROVENANCE: Purchased by the Metropolitan Museum in London, 1961.

BIBLIOGRAPHY: J. Bean, *Metropolitan Museum of Art Bulletin*, January 1962, repr. p. 160, fig. 3.

The Metropolitan Museum of Art
Rogers Fund, 61.123.2

Baccio Bandinelli

Florence 1493–Florence 1560

75 *Three Male Heads*

Pen and brown ink. 12⅝ × 8³⁄₁₆ inches (32.1 × 20.8 cm.). Several repaired holes.

Three male heads, to the left that of a youth, at center a mature bearded man, and at the right in profile a bald old man, are grouped together in a way that suggests that Bandinelli intended to represent the Three Ages of Man; the bearded man at center may be an idealized portrait of the artist. A strikingly similar grouping of three male heads occurs in Titian's so-called *Allegory of Prudence*,

formerly in the Francis Howard Collection in London (repr. Tietze, *Titian*, pl. 252). Titian's picture is often dated about 1565, that is to say after Bandinelli's death, and Bandinelli's drawing and Titian's picture no doubt derive from the same or a similar emblematic source.

PROVENANCE: Dr. Francis Springell; Springell sale, London, Sotheby's, June 28, 1962, no. 18, repr.; purchased by the Metropolitan Museum in London, 1963.

EXHIBITIONS: London, P. & D. Colnaghi, "Loan Exhibition of Drawings by Old Masters from the Collection of Dr. and Mrs. Francis Springell," 1959, no. 22, pl. XI; London, P. & D. Colnaghi, "Exhibition of Old Master Drawings," 1963, no. 9, pl. II.

The Metropolitan Museum of Art
Rogers Fund, 63.125

Jacopo da Pontormo

Pontormo 1494–Florence 1557

76 *Standing Male Nude Seen from the Back, and Two Seated Nudes*
Verso: *Striding Nude with Upraised Arms*

Red chalk (recto). Black chalk, with vestiges of white, over red chalk (verso). 16 × 8⅞ inches (40.6 × 22.5 cm.). Watermark: fruit (Briquet 7392). Stained; long repaired forked tear in lower left quadrant, other smaller tears and repairs at right margin; creases, upper center.

Inscribed in black ink at lower left, *Jacopo da Pontormo*; in brown ink at lower right corner, Crozat paraph and *334*; at upper left corner in another hand, *434*. Inscribed on verso, Crozat paraph and faintly legible number, *335*; also in pencil, *2550*.

Although Pontormo drawings more often than not are preparatory for some specific project, the studies from nude models on both sides of this sheet are not related to any known painting or fresco. On the basis of style, they can be dated about 1520–1521, the period of Pontormo's first artistic maturity that produced the lunette fresco of Vertumnus and Pomona for the great *salone* of the Medicean Villa del Poggio a Caiano. Typical in their eccentric mannerist grace and intensity, these studies still retain a degree of the naturalism of Andrea del Sarto, Pontormo's last teacher. Copies of both recto and verso, probably by Pontormo's pupil Naldini, are preserved among the drawings from the Baldinucci Collection at the Louvre (Rearick, A 330 and A 328).

The bulk of Pontormo's drawings having remained in his native Florence (186 sheets in the Uffizi, according to Rearick), it is not surprising that few unquestioned sheets are to be found in American collections. Rearick lists only four, the present drawing and three in the Fogg Museum.

PROVENANCE: Pierre Crozat (Lugt 2951); Henry Reitlinger; Reitlinger sale, London, Sotheby's, December 9, 1953, no. 84; purchased by the Pierpont Morgan Library in London, 1954.

BIBLIOGRAPHY: Alfred Scharf, "The Exhibition of Old Master Drawings at the Royal Academy," *Burlington Magazine*, XCV, 1953, p. 352, fig. 3; Morgan Library, *Fifth Fellows Report*, 1954, pp. 65–68, repr.; C. Gamba, *Contributo alla conoscenza del Pontormo*, Florence, 1956, p. 11, fig. 12; Berenson, 1961, no. 2256 H, fig. 905; Janet Cox Rearick, *The Drawings of Pontormo*, Cambridge, Massachusetts, 1964, nos. 188, 189, figs. 172, 178.

EXHIBITIONS: London, Royal Academy, "Drawings by Old Masters," 1953, no. 55, pl. 12; New York, Morgan Library, Fiftieth Anniversary Exhibition, 1957, no. 86, pl. 53; New York, Columbia Benefit Exhibition, 1959, nos. 20–21, pl. 11.

The Pierpont Morgan Library
Gift of the Fellows with the special assistance of
Anne Bigelow Stern and Janos Scholz, 1954.4

Giovanni Battista di Jacopo di Guasparre, called Rosso Fiorentino

Florence 1495–Paris 1540

77 Head of a Woman with an Elaborate Coiffure

Black chalk, certain contours reinforced in pen and brown ink, background colored in brown wash. 9¼ × 6¹⁵⁄₁₆ inches (23.5 × 17.6 cm). Top of sheet cut to the shape of an arch.

Inscribed in pen and brown ink at top center, *Rosso Fiorentino*; at upper right margin, *Giulia Gonzaga Duchezz . . . | di Mantoa*; at lower right corner, *93*.

Old inscriptions on the drawing and its mount suggest that this profile head of a woman with a rich, mannered coiffure of entwined braids and shell volutes is a portrait of Giulia Gonzaga, the celebrated Contessa di Fondi (1513–1566). It is unlikely, however, that the drawing is a portrait; the physical type is a creation of Rosso's imagination, and can be encountered in several of the artist's pictures. The elaborate and refined black chalk modeling is typical of Rosso's draughtsmanship. Pen lines that reinforce certain contours may well be additions made by the artist himself, but the brown wash that silhouettes the head is possibly a later addition.

PROVENANCE: John Talman (the drawing is on a Talman mount and is inscribed on the verso *e collectione J. Talman*); Sir Joshua Reynolds (Lugt 2364); John Fitchett Marsh (Lugt 1455); purchased by the Metropolitan Museum in London, 1952.

The Metropolitan Museum of Art
Rogers Fund, 52.124.2

Giovanni Battista Franco

Venice about 1498–Venice 1561

78 Standing Male Nude

Red chalk. 15¼ × 6⅝ inches (38.7 × 16.8 cm.). Scattered oil stains. Repairs at upper left and lower corners.

The modeling of this male figure, probably studied for a Flagellation of Christ or a Martyrdom of St. Sebastian, reveals the dominant influence of Michelangelo on Battista Franco. However, the energy of Michelangelo's draughtsmanship and of his sculptural style has been codified by Franco into a smooth and somewhat superficial, but distinctly personal formula.

PROVENANCE: Jonathan Richardson Senior (Lugt 2183); Mrs. E. E. James, London; sale, London, Sotheby's, May 16, 1962, no. 158; purchased by the Metropolitan Museum in London, 1962.

The Metropolitan Museum of Art
Rogers Fund, 62.119.10

Giulio Romano

Rome 1499–Mantua 1546

79 Arms of the Cardinal Gonzaga

Pen and brown ink over black chalk. 15⁹⁄₁₆ × 9¼ inches (39.5 × 23.5 cm.). Lined. Loss at upper right corner, crease at lower left, two long repaired tears.

Inscribed in a banderole at the top: *HERC GON CAR*. On verso, various inscriptions relating to collections and sales.

During the six years (1540–1546) that Giulio Romano served the Cardinal Ercole Gonzaga at Mantua, he made a number of drawings displaying the Cardinal's arms in various ways. According to Hartt, the vigorous pen sketch in the Morgan Library, which is somewhat heraldic in composition, is earlier than the drawings at Chatsworth and at Haarlem, both of which show the four Gonzaga eagles drawing a chariot. Other drawings of the Cardinal's arms are found at Christ Church, Oxford, and in the Ellesmere Collection at Mertoun House, Roxburghshire, Scotland.

PROVENANCE: Jonathan Richardson Senior (Lugt 2184); Sir Joshua Reynolds (Lugt 2364); Reynolds sale, London, H. Phillips, March 5, 1798, no. 1784; Charles Fairfax Murray; purchased by J. Pierpont Morgan in London, 1910.

BIBLIOGRAPHY: Fairfax Murray, IV, no. 16, repr.; Frederick Hartt, *Giulio Romano*, I, New Haven, 1958, pp. 234, 251, 252, 308, no. 361.

EXHIBITIONS: New York, Morgan Library, World's Fair, 1939, no. 73; 1940, no. 91.

The Pierpont Morgan Library
No. IV, 16

Anonymous Ferrarese Artist

End of the fifteenth century

80 *The Virgin Annunciate*

Pen and brown ink, brown wash, on parchment. 8⅛ × 3¹⁄₁₆ inches (20.7 × 7.8 cm.). Slight surface abrasions. Lined.

This drawing was exhibited at the Royal Academy in 1930 with the attribution, perhaps traditional, to Francesco del Cossa. On that occasion, A. G. B. Russell suggested the rather unlikely name of the Lombard Bernardino Butinone, and the drawing figured in the Oppenheimer Collection under this designation. Cossa, however, seems nearer the mark, for the flat, broad, metallic folds of the drapery have a distinctly Ferrarese character, as do the square face and broad hands of the figure. Ferrarese drawings of the late fifteenth century are rare, and often of problematic attribution. At the present state of our knowledge of this material it seems impossible to say anything more specific of this fine design on parchment than that it is prob-

ably by a Ferrarese, or more generally Emilian, artist not far from Cosimo Tura or Marco Zoppo.

PROVENANCE: Henry Oppenheimer, London; Oppenheimer sale, London, Christie's, July 10–14, 1936, no. 40, pl. 8 (as Butinone); purchased by the Metropolitan Museum in New York, 1964.

BIBLIOGRAPHY: Vasari Society, second series, II, 1921, no. 1, pl. 1 (as Francesco del Cossa).

EXHIBITIONS: London, Royal Academy, "Italian Art, 1200–1900," 1930, no. 619 (attributed to Cossa); London, Royal Academy, Italian Art, 1930: commemorative drawings catalogue, 1931, no. 148, pl. CXXVI B (as Butinone).

The Metropolitan Museum of Art
Gustavus A. Pfeiffer Fund, 64.137

Domenico Campagnola

Padua or Venice 1500–Padua (?) after 1552

81 *Buildings in a Rocky Landscape*

Pen and brown ink. Ruled border in dark brown ink. 6¹⁄₁₆ × 7¾ inches (15.4 × 19.6 cm.). Cut across the upper quarter; small area of abrasion just above roof of building at left. Lined.

Inscribed on verso in pen and brown ink, *S. W. 304.*

Verso: Another landscape in pen and dark brown ink is visible through the lining.

Among the large number of landscape drawings of varying quality classed generically under the Campagnola label, this sheet is one of some merit. Fairfax Murray in 1905 illustrated the drawing as Giulio Campagnola, using it, as he remarked, to point up the "vexed question" of Titian, Giorgione, and Campagnola. The Tietzes in 1944 transferred the drawing to Domenico's name, and Robert M. Walker had independently reached a similar conclusion in his doctoral dissertation ("Domenico Campagnola: Landscape Draughtsman of the Sixteenth Century," Harvard University, 1941). Professor Walker, on the basis of quite recent examination of the comparative material in the Uffizi and the Albertina, reconfirms that the Morgan drawing should be assigned to the early period of Domenico when the influence of both Titian and of Giulio Campagnola is apparent.

The Tietzes' description of the drawing as "somewhat damaged" refers to the cut across the upper quarter and a small abraded area above the roof of the left building. The design area of the drawing is, nevertheless, relatively unaffected. The sheet must have been trimmed along the right margin since the pennant flying at the right is incomplete.

PROVENANCE: Charles Fairfax Murray; purchased by J. Pierpont Morgan in London, 1910.

BIBLIOGRAPHY: Fairfax Murray, I, no. 59, repr. (as Giulio Campagnola); R. E. Fry, *Vasari Society*, first series, II, 1906–1907, under no. 11 (as school of Giorgione); Tietze, *Venetian Drawings*, no. 506, pl. LXXXI.

EXHIBITIONS: New York, Pierpont Morgan Library, "Landscape Drawings & Water-Colors, Bruegel to Cézanne," 1953, no. 9, pl. III; Toronto, Art Gallery of Toronto, "Titian, Tintoretto, Paolo Veronese," 1960, no. 57.

The Pierpont Morgan Library No. I, 59

Benvenuto Cellini

Florence 1500–Florence 1571

82 *Standing Nude Male Figure with a Club*

Pen and brown ink, brown wash. 16⅛ × 7¾ inches (40.9 × 19.7 cm.).

Inscribed in pen and brown ink at lower right, *alla porta di fontana | Bellio. di bronzo p piu | di dua volte il vivo . . . | erano dua variati* (at the portal of Fontainebleau, in bronze twice life-size—there were two versions).

In his autobiography, Cellini describes in some detail his model of a sculptured portal for the Château de Fontainebleau. The scheme involved a lunette containing a reclining figure of the Nymph of Fontainebleau that surmounted a rectangular opening flanked by caryatids. "Instead of columns . . . I fashioned two satyrs, one upon each side. The first of these was in somewhat more than half-relief, lifting one hand to support the cornice and holding a thick club in the other; his face was fiery and menacing, instilling fear into the beholders. . . . Though I call them satyrs, they showed nothing of the satyr except little horns and a goatish head; all the rest of the form was human." (*Autobiography*, tr. J. A. Symonds, New York, 1927, p. 272.) This elaborate drawing corresponds exactly with Cel-

lini's description, and the inscription, very possibly in the artist's own hand, specifically associates the drawing with the Fontainebleau portal. This undertaking never, presumably, reached completion, and all that remains of the portal is the bronze lunette with the Nymph of Fontainebleau now preserved in the Louvre. The style of the drawing is close to that of the only other surviving sheet that can be connected with Cellini's stay in France, a black chalk study in the Louvre for an over life-size silver statue of Juno, one of a series of twelve projected statue-candelabra designed for François I (repr. E. Camesasca, *Tutta l'opera del Cellini*, Milan, 1955, pl. 17). The Louvre drawing is identified as a candelabra project by an inscription in the same hand as that on the present drawing.

PROVENANCE: John Barnard (Lugt 1419); Sir Thomas Lawrence (Lugt 2445).

EXHIBITIONS: Newark, Old Master Drawings, 1960, no. 25, repr.

Ian Woodner

Camillo Boccaccino

Cremona 1501–Cremona 1546

83 *The Prophet Isaiah and King David with a Viola*

Pen and brown ink, brown wash, heightened with white, on light brown washed paper. 11⁷⁄₁₀ × 9¹⁵⁄₁₀ inches (29 × 25.2 cm.). Architectural contours incised with a stylus.

Study for a pair of organ shutters in the church of S. Vincenzo at Piacenza, signed by Camillo and dated 1630 (repr. Mina Gregori, *Paragone*, IV, 1953, no. 37, figs. 3 and 4). The identification of the drawing, splendid testimony to the originality of this Cremonese master, is due to John Gere, who connected it with the Piacenza organ shutters.

PROVENANCE: A. Viggiano (Lugt S. 1914).

EXHIBITIONS: Oakland, Scholz Exhibition, 1956, no. 5, repr.; Detroit, Drawings of the Italian Renaissance, 1960, no. 36, repr.; Hamburg, Scholz Exhibition, 1963, no. 19, pl. 23; New Haven, Scholz Exhibition, 1964, no. 27, pl. 8 and cover (detail).

Janos Scholz

Piero Buonaccorsi, called Perino del Vaga

Florence 1501–Rome 1547

84   *The Presentation of the Virgin*

Pen and brown ink, brown wash, heightened with white, squared in black chalk, on brownish paper. The empty triangular corners are tinted in gray-green wash, the right diagonal border tinted in gray wash. $8^{15}/_{16} \times 10^{1}/_{16}$ inches (22.7 × 25.5 cm.).

It was probably early in the third decade of the sixteenth century that Perino del Vaga was commissioned by Cardinal Lorenzo Pucci to ornament the chapel in the left transept of the Trinità dei Monti in Rome. Perino's frescoes high up on the vault of this chapel have survived in a damaged state, but the rest of the work remained unfinished when the artist left Rome for Genoa in 1527, and the decoration was completed a good deal later by Taddeo and Federico Zuccaro. On the four segments of the cross vault Perino painted scenes from the life of the Virgin. Preparatory drawings for three of these compositions—the *Meeting at the Golden Gate*, the *Birth of the Virgin*, and the *Annunciation*—have been identified in the Albertina and the Louvre (repr. Maria Vittoria Brugnoli, "Gli Affreschi di Perin del Vaga nella Cappella Pucci," *Bollettino d'Arte*, October-December 1962, figs. 9, 10, 11). The present drawing, a study for the segment with the *Presentation of the Virgin in the Temple*, has only recently reappeared. Like the Albertina drawing for the *Meeting at the Golden Gate*, it was once in the collection of Sir Thomas Lawrence.

PROVENANCE: Prince Borghese, Rome (according to Lawrence Gallery catalogue); Sir Thomas Lawrence; Samuel Woodburn, London; Woodburn sale, London, Christie's, June 4–8, 1860, no. 981; sale, London, Sotheby's, March 12, 1963, no. 20, bought by the Metropolitan Museum.

BIBLIOGRAPHY: *The Lawrence Gallery. Fifth Exhibition*, p. 30, no. 89; Bernice Davidson, "Early Drawings by Perino del Vaga—I," *Master Drawings*, I, no. 3, 1963, p. 16, pl. 7a; Bean, *100 European Drawings*, no. 19, repr.

The Metropolitan Museum of Art Rogers Fund, 63.75.1

85   *The Pool of Bethesda*

Pen and brown ink over red chalk. Diameter 8 inches (20.4 cm.). No watermark. The drawing has been extended across the bottom.

Verso: Left half of composition traced in pen and brown ink; fragment of a laurel-crowned figure, in pen and brown ink and brown wash, on extension.

This drawing and No. 86, originally part of a set of six, were made by Perino for Cardinal Alessandro Farnese as designs to be engraved in rock-crystal plaques by the lapidary and medalist Giovanni Bernardi. Five of Giovanni's six crystals, which are described by Vasari, are known today. Two are in the Museum of Industrial Art at Copenhagen, and three—among them the *Pool of Bethesda*—are found in candlesticks in the Treasury of St. Peter's. Five of the drawings are also known, the other three being divided between the Louvre (R. F. 1870:539) and the Staatliche Graphische Sammlung, Munich (Nos. 2485 and 2504). As Gere has demonstrated, the drawings are of heightened interest in that they appear to be circular adaptations of Perino's now vanished frescoes for the Massimi Chapel in the Trinità dei Monti.

Since the letter of Giovanni Bernardi indicates that the crystals for the candlesticks were carried out in 1539 (see Vilhelm Slomann, "Rock-Crystals by Giovanni Bernardi," *Burlington Magazine*, XLIX, 1926, p. 19), the drawings must have been executed just before that time.

The group of Christ and the Cripple also occurs in a drawing in the British Museum, a rectangular composition with a further figure at the left (Pouncey–Gere, no. 169, pl. 138).

The *Pool of Bethesda* was first recognized as the work of Perino by Otto Benesch at the time of a visit to the Morgan Library in 1940. Curiously enough, Fairfax Murray, who properly identified the related drawing, No. 86 of the exhibition, ascribed the present sheet to Parmigianino, probably on the basis of the chiaroscuro woodcut that Bartsch had described as being after Parmigianino (XII, p. 38, no. 14).

PROVENANCE: Sir Peter Lely (Lugt 2092); Giovanni Matteo Marchetti, bishop of Arezzo (according to Fairfax Murray); John Talman (the drawing is on a Talman mount); Charles Fairfax Murray; purchased by J. Pierpont Morgan in London, 1910.

BIBLIOGRAPHY: Fairfax Murray, IV, no. 47, repr. (as Parmigianino); J. A. Gere, "Two Late Fresco Cycles by Perino del Vaga: the Massimi Chapel and the Sala Paolina," *Burlington Magazine*, CII, 1960, p. 13, fig. 12; Philip Pouncey and J. A. Gere, *Italian Drawings . . . in the British Museum, Raphael and his Circle*, London, 1962, p. 99 under no. 169.

The Pierpont Morgan Library
No. IV, 47

86 *Miracle of the Loaves and Fishes*

Pen and brown ink, brown wash, heightened with white. Diameter 8⅜ inches (21.2 cm.). Scattered small losses. Lined.

See No. 85 above. Giovanni Bernardi's crystal of this subject has not been found.

PROVENANCE: Charles Fairfax Murray; purchased by J. Pierpont Morgan in London, 1910.

BIBLIOGRAPHY: Fairfax Murray, I, no. 21, repr.; J. A. Gere, "Two Late Fresco Cycles by Perino del Vaga: the Massimi Chapel and the Sala Paolina," *Burlington Magazine*, CII, 1960, p. 13, fig. 10.

EXHIBITIONS: Toronto, Inaugural Exhibition, 1926, no. 26, repr.

The Pierpont Morgan Library
No. I, 21

87 *Prudence*

Pen and brown ink, gray wash, over traces of black chalk. 10⅛ × 5½ inches (25.7 × 14 cm.).

Inscribed in pen and brown ink at lower right, *P.D.V.*

As Bernice Davidson was the first to point out, this is a study for the allegorical figure of Prudence, part of Perino's frescoed decoration of the Sala Paolina in the Castel S. Angelo in Rome. A few drawings by Perino for this very late decorative scheme, executed in the 1540s, have survived; one in a private collection in London, a study for the grisaille panel representing *Alexander the Great Placing in Safety the Writings of Homer*, bears an inscribed monogram, *P.D.V.*, similar to that on the present drawing. The London drawing is reproduced and the frescoes are discussed by J. A. Gere, *Burlington Magazine*, CII, 1960, pp. 9–19.

PROVENANCE: Cavaliere Gelosi (?) (Lugt 545); Professor J. Isaacs, London; Isaacs sale, London, Sotheby's, February

27, 1964, no. 15, repr.; purchased by the Metropolitan Museum in London, 1964.

The Metropolitan Museum of Art
Rogers Fund, 64.179

Francesco Mazzola, called Parmigianino

Parma 1503–Casalmaggiore 1540

88 *Three Putti*

Pen and brown ink, brown wash, and red chalk, left figure squared in lead, ruled border in black ink. 6³⁄₁₆ × 6⅛ inches (15.7 × 15.6 cm.). No watermark.

Inscribed in pen and brown ink on mount, *Parmegiano.*

Verso: Black chalk sketch of Diana dashing water into the face of Actaeon, touches of red chalk.

Two of the three putti appear with little or no change in the frescoes decorating the vaulting of the small chamber in the Rocca of Fontanellato. The central figure occurs in the spandrel immediately above the two dogs on the wall showing Actaeon and a companion pursuing a nymph (Freedberg, fig. 22); the left, in the spandrel between the stag-headed Actaeon and the splashing Diana (Freedberg, fig. 23). A preliminary black chalk sketch for this last scene, with the composition fitted to a spandrel rather than a lunette and showing Actaeon in contemporary dress, is on the verso of the Morgan drawing. Other studies for the Fontanellato putti are found at the British Museum, Chatsworth, and the Louvre.

A. E. Popham in *Master Drawings* has recently plausibly proposed that a drawing in Berlin (no. 489) preserves an idea for the decoration of the walls, as opposed to the vaulting, of the same chamber. He also puts forth the suggestion that the commission may have been given to the artist by Galeazzo Sanvitale, Lord of Fontanellato, before 1521 but was not completed until just before Parmigianino's departure for Rome early in 1524. Freedberg suggested a date of 1523.

The Morgan drawing was engraved by Hendrik van der Borcht in 1637 as two separate sheets.

PROVENANCE: Earl of Arundel; N. F. Haym (Lugt 1970); The Earls Spencer (Lugt 1530); Charles Fairfax Murray; purchased by J. Pierpont Morgan in London, 1910.

BIBLIOGRAPHY: Fairfax Murray, I, no. 49, repr.; Lili Fröhlich-Bum, *Parmigianino und der Manierismus*, Vienna, 1921, p. 192; Giovanni Copertini, *Il Parmigianino*, I, Parma, 1932, p. 56; Lili Fröhlich-Bum, "Unpublished Drawings by Parmigianino," *Old Master Drawings*, IX, 1935, pp. 56–57, fig. 11; Charles de Tolnay, *History and Techniques of Old Master Drawings*, New York, 1943, no. 100, repr.; Armando O. Quintavalle, *Il Parmigianino*, Milan, 1948, pp. 150, 181, n. 64, p. 199; Freedberg, *Parmigianino*, p. 162, n. 44, p. 164, pl. 29; Popham, *Parmigianino*, pp. 24–25, 55, pl. 13 (verso only); A. E. Popham, "Drawings by Parmigianino for the Rocca of Fontanellato," *Master Drawings*, I, no. 1, 1963, pp. 5–6, 10, n. 14, pl. 5a (verso only).

EXHIBITIONS: Hartford, Morgan Treasures, 1960, no. 69; Northampton, Smith College, Italian Drawings, 1941, no. 39; Oberlin, Oberlin College, Allen Memorial Art Museum, "Youthful Works by Great Artists," 1963, no. 7, repr. (catalogue in *Allen Memorial Art Museum Bulletin*, XX, 1963, no. 3).

The Pierpont Morgan Library
No. I, 49

89 *Three Studies of Putti and of a Seated Boy*

Red chalk. 7³⁄₁₆ × 5¹³⁄₁₆ inches (18.3 × 14.8 cm.).

Verso: Studies in red chalk of a woman's head, of a putto, and of a fence.

Parmigianino's purpose in making these beautiful red chalk sketches is unknown, for they cannot be related to any surviving work. On stylistic grounds A. E. Popham dates them early in the artist's career, before or just after his departure for Rome about 1524.

EXHIBITIONS: Bloomington, Scholz Exhibition, 1958, no. 35, repr.; Hamburg, Scholz Exhibition, 1963, no. 108, pl. 22; New Haven, Scholz Exhibition, 1964, no. 43, repr. no. 10.

Janos Scholz

90 *The Holy Family with Angels and Shepherds*

Pen and brown ink, brown wash, some corrections with white. 10⁵⁄₁₆ × 7³⁄₈ inches (26.2 × 18.8 cm.). Watermark: IHS surmounted by a cross.

Verso: Musical notations in the artist's hand.

In a recent communication, A. E. Popham stated that the *Holy Family* is stylistically close to the Louvre *Lamentation* (Inv. 6393; "Dessins de l'École de Parme," 1964, no. 50, pl. XI), which has on the verso a study almost certainly made for the Madrid *Holy Family* (Freedberg, *Parmigianino*, fig. 35), a painting datable in the artist's pre-Roman period. The Currier drawing is by analogy, therefore, to be regarded as a work of the early Parma period, a date also supported by the watermark, which is one found on the drawings of Correggio and of the young Parmigianino.

BIBLIOGRAPHY: H. M. Calmann (Catalogue, London, 1964), no. 6, pl. 6.

Stephen Currier

91 *The Adoration of the Shepherds*

Pen and brown ink, brown wash, heightened with white on brown washed paper. 8½ × 5¹⁵⁄₁₆ inches (21.6 × 14.1 cm.). Vertical and horizontal folds at center.

Parmigianino arrived in Rome in 1524 and was active there until the sack of the city in 1527. From these years probably dates a group of free and spirited drawings in which he studied a number of alternative compositional schemes for an Adoration of the Shepherds where the Virgin is represented bathing the Infant Christ. In addition to the present sheet, drawings in the Uffizi (747E), the British Museum (1853-10-8-3 and 1856-6-14-2 verso), the École des Beaux-Arts in Paris (37143), and the Louvre (Inv. 6385) have been related by Mrs. Burroughs and by Popham to these compositional researches. Important and inventive variants distinguish these designs, although the seated cross-legged figure of St. Joseph pointing up at the flying angel in the Metropolitan Museum's drawing also occurs in the Louvre sketch. None of the drawings gives us the solution used by Parmigianino in the *Adoration of the Shepherds*, a picture datable in his Roman period, now in the Doria Pamphilj Gallery (repr. Freedberg, fig. 46). The present drawing was engraved in reverse by Metz in 1798. An old copy of the drawing is in the Horne Foundation (repr. Licia Ragghianti Collobi, *Disegni della Fondazione Horne in Firenze*, Florence, 1963, p. 24, no. 64, pl. 39, wrongly attributed to Pellegrino Tibaldi).

PROVENANCE: Paignon-Dijonval; Vicomte Morel de Vindé, Paris; Sir Thomas Lawrence (Lugt 2445); William Coningham (Lugt 476); Dr. Frederic Haussman, Berlin; purchased by the Metropolitan Museum in New York, 1946.

BIBLIOGRAPHY: Metz, *Imitations of Drawings*, repr. p. 72; M. Bénard, *Cabinet de M. Paignon-Dijonval, état détaillé et raisonné des dessins et estampes dont il est composé*, Paris, 1810, p. 26, no. 391 (the folds in the sheet are mentioned); *The Lawrence Gallery. Fourth Exhibition*, p. 9, no. 14; Lili Fröhlich-Bum, *Parmigianino und der Manierismus*, Vienna, 1921, p. 95, repr. from Metz's facsimile, fig. 113; Giovanni Copertini, *Il Parmigianino*, II, Parma, 1932, p. 60, repr. from Metz's facsimile, pl. CXLIIa; Louise Burroughs, "A Drawing by Francesco Mazzola, Il Parmigianino," *Metropolitan Museum of Art Bulletin*, December 1948, pp. 101 ff., repr. p. 102; Freedberg, *Parmigianino*, p. 171, fig. 47; Bean, *100 European Drawings*, no. 20, repr.

*The Metropolitan Museum of Art
Rogers Fund, 46.80.3*

92 Study for a Marriage of the Virgin

Pen and brown ink, red chalk, and pale brown wash. 7 × 9⅛ inches (17.8 × 23.1 cm.). Watermark: IHS (Briquet 9462).

During his years in Rome (1524–1527), Parmigianino supplied several designs to Jacopo Caraglio for engraving, among them a composition of the Marriage of the Virgin showing the strong impress of Rosso's painting of the same subject in S. Lorenzo, Florence. The finished drawing used for the engraving (Bartsch, XV, p. 66, no. 1) is at Chatsworth (Popham, no. 26), and there is an old copy in the Louvre (Inv. 6543). The present drawing is a study for the figures of the spectators in the foreground of the Chatsworth sheet. The woman at the left seems to have been inspired by Michelangelo's Libyan Sibyl; that on the right by the Persian Sibyl. A pure pen sketch, on a much smaller scale, for the group of the Virgin, Joseph, and the High Priest is also in the Morgan Library (I, 46 B).

PROVENANCE: Baron Dominique Vivant-Denon (Lugt 780); Charles Fairfax Murray; purchased by J. Pierpont Morgan in London, 1910.

BIBLIOGRAPHY: Fairfax Murray, I, no. 48, repr.; Vivant-Denon, *Monuments*, III, pl. 163; F. Antal, "Un Capolavoro inedito del Parmigianino," *Pinacotheca*, I, 1928, p. 52; Armando O. Quintavalle, *Il Parmigianino*, Milan, 1948, pp. 66, 82, n. 42, p. 196; Freedberg, *Parmigianino*, pp. 65, 174, pl. 40; Popham, *Parmigianino*, p. 58, under no. 26; *Old Master Drawings from Chatsworth*, exhibition circulated by the Smithsonian Institution, 1962–1963, p. 25 under no. 42.

*The Pierpont Morgan Library
No. I, 48*

93 The Infant Christ Asleep on the Lap of the Virgin

Red chalk over preliminary indications with the stylus. 7½ × 5¹¹⁄₁₆ inches (19 × 14.4 cm.). No watermark. Small tear and repaired losses along right margin.

Verso: Pen sketch of antique statue of standing male nude (Hercules?) and, in opposite direction, detail of torso of Virgin in pen and gray-brown wash.

The evolution of Parmigianino's design for his celebrated *Madonna dal collo lungo*, Pitti Gallery, Florence, commissioned by Elena Baiardi on December 23, 1534, for her chapel in the Chiesa dei Servi di Maria in Parma, is traceable today in at least twenty drawings, according to Popham's latest count. These include the drawing at Budapest that Popham identified as a possible first study for the Child (*Bulletin du Musée National Hongrois des Beaux-Arts*, 1961, no. 19, p. 54, fig. 38) and the previously unknown sheet recently acquired by the National Gallery of Canada.

The Morgan drawing belongs to the definitive later stages of the artist's planning and shows him concentrating on the figure of the Infant Christ in a position very near to the final solution. Eventually, in the painting he would show the Virgin's hand supporting the Child's head rather than the body, His right arm, out of view in the drawing, stretching upward along His mother's sleeve, and the left leg resting across her knee instead of hanging relaxed. Since the Child's head is one of several small unfinished passages in the painting (which was not placed in the chapel until 1542, after Parmigianino's death), the airy ringlets that crown the Child's sleeping countenance in the drawing reveal the intent to soften the bald cranium we today see in the picture.

Freedberg has withdrawn his doubts about the authenticity of the drawing, partly on the basis of the Rosaspino engraving, which is very close to the drawing and, probably, as Popham suspects, made after it with the head added. If so, the collection of Giovanni Antonio Armano, where Rosaspino found his model, should be added to the provenance of the Morgan sheet.

PROVENANCE: Sir James Knowles; Charles Fairfax Murray; purchased by J. Pierpont Morgan in London, 1910.

BIBLIOGRAPHY: Fairfax Murray, IV, no. 42, repr.; Tietze, *European Master Drawings*, no. 39, repr.; Freedberg, *Parmigianino*, pp. 188, 254; Popham, *Parmigianino*, p. 42; Robert Wark, "A Sheet of Studies by Parmigianino," *Art Quarterly*, XXIII, 1959, p. 246; A. E. Popham, "Two Drawings by Parmigianino," *National Gallery of Canada Bulletin*, II, 1964, no. 2, pp. 24, 30.

EXHIBITIONS: Buffalo, Master Drawings, 1935, no. 31, repr.; San Francisco, "Golden Gate International Exposition, Master Drawings," 1940, no. 75, repr.; Northampton, Smith College, Italian Drawings, 1941, no. 41; Worcester, Fiftieth Anniversary Exhibition, 1948, no. 35; Newark, Old Master Drawings, 1960, no. 12, repr.; Cambridge, Fogg Art Museum, Anxiety and Elegance, 1962, no. 18.

The Pierpont Morgan Library
No. IV, 42

94 *Studies for the Figure of Moses*
Verso: *Studies for the Figure of Eve and Architectural Studies*

Pen and brown ink, brown wash, over slight traces of black chalk, on light brown paper. 8¼ × 6 1/16 inches (21 × 15.4 cm.).

These sketches of the figure of Moses holding aloft the Tables of the Law and of Eve seizing the fatal apple are studies for part of one of Parmigianino's major commissions, the decoration of the eastern apse and vaulting of the church of S. Maria della Steccata in Parma. Other preparatory drawings—studies for individual figures and of the whole scheme—exist in the British Museum, the Louvre, Chatsworth, and elsewhere, and they reveal how elaborate were the artist's preparations for the project and how many alternative solutions came to his mind. Unfortunately, the artist was not as conscientious in his execution as in his preparation. He received the commission in 1531 with the understanding that the frescoes were to be completed within eighteen months. In 1535 the work was still unfinished, indeed hardly begun, and in 1539 Parmigianino was arrested on the order of his exasperated patrons. He escaped from Parma and died in exile the following year. The figures of Moses and the studies of Eve on the verso of the sheet are both related to the very small part of the decoration that was completed by Parmigianino himself. Moses and Eve appear painted in monochrome on

the ribs of the vault of the eastern chapel of the church (repr. Freedberg, *Parmigianino*, figs. 99, 101).

PROVENANCE: Earl of Arundel; Antonio Maria Zanetti, Venice (according to the Lawrence Gallery catalogue); Baron Dominique Vivant-Denon (Lugt 779); Sir Thomas Lawrence (Lugt 2445); Captain Richard Ford; Ford sale, London, Sotheby's, April 25, 1934, no. 29; Sir Bruce Ingram; purchased by the Metropolitan Museum in London, 1962.

BIBLIOGRAPHY: Vivant-Denon, *Monuments*, III, pl. 157 (recto and verso in reverse); *The Lawrence Gallery. Fourth Edition*, p. 10, no. 21; Popham, *Parmigianino*, pp. 21, 40, 64, pls. LVI (recto), LVII (verso); J. Bean, *Metropolitan Museum of Art Bulletin*, March 1963, pp. 231–232, figs. 3 (recto), 4 (verso); Bean, *100 European Drawings*, no. 21, repr.

EXHIBITIONS: Montreal, Five Centuries of Drawings, 1953, no. 46, repr.; Amsterdam, Rijksmuseum, "Le Triomphe du maniérisme européen," 1955, no. 231; London, Royal Academy, "Italian Art and Britain," 1960, no. 468; Rotterdam/Amsterdam, "150 Tekeningen uit vier Eeuwen uit de Verzameling van Sir Bruce en Lady Ingram," 1961–1962, no. 142, pl. 2 (verso).

The Metropolitan Museum of Art
Gustavus A. Pfeiffer Fund, 62.135

95 *Interior of a Painter's Studio*

Pen and brown ink, ruled border in black ink. 5½ × 4⅞ inches (14.1 × 12.5 cm.). No watermark. Very small tears at edges; slight blurring of design at left and right margins caused by dampness. Lined with transparent paper.

Inscribed in an old (sixteenth-century?) hand in pen and brown ink at lower center, *parmesan*.

The significance of this drawing has yet to be explained. It is most likely no more concerned with the faithful representation of an artist's studio than Picasso's artist-model sequences. It offers an interesting comparison with the background scene at the left in Vasari's painting *The Forge of Vulcan* in the Uffizi, where in a similar vaulted chamber nude draughtsmen are at work and a boy carries a bit of sculpture on his head. In the Morgan drawing one can distinguish a draughtsman and painter at the left, a perspective expert with his long rule and compasses on the right, and a sculptor with various small models toward the rear of the long narrow vaulted room. The relaxed central figure resting his arm on a book might seem to be the patron about whom the arts of design revolve.

The date of the drawing is conjectural. As Popham says, it is most likely a late rather than an early work.

PROVENANCE: Sir Thomas Lawrence (Lugt 2445); Charles Fairfax Murray; purchased by J. Pierpont Morgan in London, 1910.

BIBLIOGRAPHY: Fairfax Murray, IV, no. 46, repr.; Popham, *Parmigianino*, pp. 43, 66, pl. 65.

EXHIBITIONS: Northampton, Smith College, Italian Drawings, 1941, no. 27; Indianapolis, Pontormo to Greco, 1954, no. 23, repr.; Detroit, Drawings of the Italian Renaissance, 1960, no. 26.

The Pierpont Morgan Library
No. IV, 46

Francesco Primaticcio

Bologna 1504–Paris 1570

96 Seated Figure of Faith

Black chalk, heightened with white on light gray-brown paper. 12 × 7 inches (30.4 × 17.7 cm.). The sheet has been trimmed at the sides so that it tapers at the top to 2⅟₁₆ inches (5.2 cm.). No watermark. The artist has made a change in the head by pasting a second version over the first. The silhouetted arched top has been extended to form a rectangle.

Inscribed in pen and brown ink at lower left over an earlier inscription in chalk, *Giovanni Battista da Bologna*; in pencil in another hand, *g z*. Inscribed on verso in pen and ink at lower right, *Rugiero del 'Abati | 5.3*.

The lightly indicated chalice that the seated woman holds in her left hand identifies her as Faith, one of the three Theological Virtues. It is known from various sources that Primaticcio designed several series of the Virtues during his long career in France, but, since none survives in finished form, it is difficult to link the present drawing with any of them. Judging from the disparity in scale and style between this drawing and the *Temperance* in the British Museum, which Anthony Blunt (*Art and Architecture in France*, London, 1953, pl. 42) associates with the panels painted for the armoires of the Cabinet du Roi at Fontainebleau decorated between 1541 and 1545, the Morgan sheet is not related to this project. Other possibilities include the representations of the Virtues in the decorations

of the gallery at the Hôtel de Montmorency, rue Sainte-Avoie, Paris, painted by Niccolò dell' Abbate after the designs of Primaticcio (H. Sauval, *Histoire et recherche . . .* , 1742), and two sculptural commissions featuring the Virtues, the tomb of the Guises and that of Henry II.

The alteration of the head is clearly the work of Primaticcio himself. Apparently dissatisfied with its original position, probably more nearly a profile view, he executed another head and pasted it over the first version. Possibly he drew the second head on an upper corner of the sheet on which the figure itself is executed and then cut it out; if so, this might account for the sheet's tapered shape.

PROVENANCE: Sir Peter Lely (Lugt 2092); sale, London, Sotheby's, February 22, 1961, no. 33 (one of lot of four); purchased by the Pierpont Morgan Library in London, 1961.

BIBLIOGRAPHY: Morgan Library, *Eleventh Fellows Report*, 1961, pp. 75–78, repr.

The Pierpont Morgan Library
Gift of the Fellows, 1961.15

97 Vulcan Forging the Darts of Cupid

Red chalk, heightened with white, on brownish paper. 13⅜ × 17⅖₁₆ inches (35 × 43.7 cm.). Sheet cut to the shape of a spandrel; vertical crease at center. Lined.

Like No. 98, an elaborate preparatory study for two of the spandrels in the Salle de Bal at Fontainebleau. The painted decorations of this room, which survive in a disastrously reworked state, were executed between 1552 and 1556. Primaticcio supplied the designs for the frescoes, but the painting is said to have been largely the work of his talented assistant Niccolò dell' Abbate. The most conspicuous features in Primaticcio's decorative scheme were the eight broad spandrels above the windows. In addition to the present drawings four other designs for the spandrels survive: a study for *Apollo and the Muses on Mount Parnassus* in the British Museum (1900-6-11-4) and drawings for a *Bacchanal* and *Ceres Presiding over the Harvest* at Chantilly (repr. Louis Dimier, *Le Primatice*, Paris, 1928, pls. X, XI). Recently Dr. Fenyő has identified at Budapest a study for the spandrel *Phaeton in Supplication before Apollo* (Iván Fenyő, "Dessins italiens inconnus du XVᵉ siècle," *Bulletin du Musée National Hongrois des Beaux-Arts*, no. 22, 1963, pp. 97, 98, pl. 54).

PROVENANCE: Prosper Henry Lankrink (Lugt 2090); Earls of Pembroke; Pembroke sale, London, Sotheby's, July 5–10, 1917, no. 500, bought by the Metropolitan Museum.

BIBLIOGRAPHY: Strong, *Wilton House Drawings*, Part V, repr. no. 52; Metropolitan Museum, *European Drawings*, I. repr. no. 25; Bean, *100 European Drawings*, no. 22, repr.

EXHIBITIONS: New London, Fourth Anniversary Exhibition, 1936, no. 48, repr.; Cambridge, Fogg Art Museum, Anxiety and Elegance, 1962, no. 28.

The Metropolitan Museum of Art
Hewitt Fund, 19.76.7

98 *Discord at the Marriage Feast of Peleus and Thetis*

Red chalk, heightened with white, on brownish paper. 12½ × 17⅟₁₆ inches (31.6 × 43.4 cm.). Vertical crease and blue chalk line at center; repairs at left. Lined.

Inscribed in pen and brown ink at lower right, *Primaticcio*.

See No. 97 above (also for provenance).

BIBLIOGRAPHY: Strong, *Wilton House Drawings*, Part V, repr. no. 53; Metropolitan Museum, *European Drawings*, I, repr. no. 24.

The Metropolitan Museum of Art
Hewitt Fund, 19.76.6

Pomponio Amalteo

Motta di Livenza 1505–S. Vito al Tagliamento 1588

99 *The Flight into Egypt*

Pen and brown ink, brown wash over black chalk, faintly heightened with white, on blue paper. 8¼ × 9⅟₁₆ inches (21 × 23.9 cm.). No watermark.

Inscribed in pen and brown ink at lower center, *del amateo*. Inscribed on verso in black chalk at lower center, *Pomponio ... Amalteo*; in pen and brown ink at lower right, *Pomponio Amalteo Friuli / Disc. e Genero del Pordenone / ... il suo fratello Girola.* Various inscriptions concerning former collections.

Verso: Black chalk studies of drapery, of a nude figure, and of a Virgin and Child.

The evidence of the old inscriptions taken in conjunction with the general conformity of this drawing with the artist's painting style makes it a key piece for the identification of the draughtsmanship of Pomponio Amalteo, who was a pupil and son-in-law of Pordenone. Popham calls attention to a presumably signed drawing by Amalteo illustrated as the first plate in R. W. P. de Vries's catalogue no. 2, 1929.

The *pentimenti* in the arms of the figure of Joseph indicate that the artist contemplated an alternate solution showing Joseph pulling down the branch of the palm tree for whose fruit the Child reaches.

PROVENANCE: Jonathan Richardson Junior (Lugt 2170); Richard Cosway (Lugt 629); William Esdaile (Lugt 2617); Thomas Thane (Lugt 2461); Sir John Charles Robinson (Lugt 1433); sale of a Well-known Amateur [Sir John Charles Robinson], London, Christie's, May 12–14, 1902, no. 5; Charles Fairfax Murray; purchased by J. Pierpont Morgan in London, 1910.

BIBLIOGRAPHY: Fairfax Murray, IV, no. 70, repr.; Tietze, *Venetian Drawings*, no. 23, pl. xcv, 1; Popham–Wilde, *Italian Drawings at Windsor*, p. 301 under no. 745.

The Pierpont Morgan Library
No. IV, 70

Leone Leoni, attributed to

Menaggio 1509–Milan 1590

100 *Profile Studies of the Head of Andrea Doria; Three Smaller Sketches of a Horse Tamer*

Pen and brown ink. 5⅟₅₁₆ × 7⅟₃₁₆ inches (15.1 × 19.8 cm.). Watermark: fragmentary, two crossed arrows.

Inscribed in brown ink at upper right in a sixteenth-century hand, *andreae doriae*.

Verso: Pen and brown ink profile of Doria, ink counterproof of the upper part of a coat of arms, and a centaur in red chalk.

The basis for the attribution of this sheet to Leoni is its association with the medal of Andrea Doria made by the Lombard sculptor in 1541 in token of gratitude for his release from the galleys by the famous Genoese admiral. The sculptor had been condemned to the galleys for the fatal wounding of a quarrelsome rival. Until Leoni's style as a draughtsman is fully established, the possibility cannot be overlooked that these vital sketches of the leonine head—made surely, if not in the presence of the great man, in immediate recollection of an interview—are from the hand of another artist working in Genoa at this period. Doria employed a number of artists in Genoa including Beccafumi, Perino del Vaga, Pordenone, and Girolamo da Treviso.

PROVENANCE: Paul Adaneidi Frasheri Bey; purchased by the Pierpont Morgan Library in London, 1960.

BIBLIOGRAPHY: Morgan Library, *Tenth Fellows Report, 1960*, pp. 48–50, repr.

The Pierpont Morgan Library
Gift of the Fellows, 1960.11

Francesco dei Rossi, called Francesco Salviati

Florence 1510–Rome 1563

101 A Pope Enthroned Presenting an Object to a Kneeling Warrior

Pen and brown ink, brown wash, heightened with white, over a little black chalk. Horizontal pen line at center; several layers of *pentimenti* pasted on in foreground. 8¼ × 10⁷⁄₁₆ inches (21 × 26.5 cm.).

In this hastily indicated scheme, a vast crowd of spectators watches as a pope presents an orblike object to a kneeling warrior; monuments reminiscent of Rome are visible in the background. Salviati, whose nervous, schematic pen work is seen here in its most abbreviated form, has made corrections in the foreground by pasting on several areas of *pentimenti*. Richard Wunder has suggested that the drawing may be a study for a fresco on one of the long walls of the Salotto in the Palazzo Farnese in Rome, where Salviati represented Pope Eugene IV giving the baton of papal commandment to Ranuccio Farnese (repr. Hermann Voss, *Die Malerei der Spätrenaissance in Rom und Florenz*, I, Berlin, 1920, fig. 89). The Cooper Union drawing may indeed be connected with the early stages of Salviati's planning for the Palazzo Farnese decoration, but the finished fresco contains only eleven figures. A group of drawings by Salviati at Windsor representing scenes in the history of the papacy are related stylistically to the present sheet (Popham–Wilde, *Italian Drawings at Windsor*, nos. 888–890).

PROVENANCE: Giovanni Piancastelli, Rome.

EXHIBITIONS: New York, American Federation of Arts, "Five Centuries of Drawings. The Cooper Union Centennial Exhibition" (catalogue by Richard P. Wunder), 1959–1961, no. 4.

The Cooper Union Museum
1901-39-1365

102 Head and Shoulders of a Bearded Man

Black chalk. 11¹³⁄₁₆ × 9⁷⁄₁₆ inches (30.1 × 24 cm.). No watermark. Crease at right margin, small repaired losses at left corners.

Inscribed on verso in pen and brown ink, *Salviati*; in pencil, *m. heemskerk*. Accompanying the drawing is an inscription in brown ink in the hand of Jonathan Richardson Junior, presumably removed from an old mount: *Baccio Bandinelli | Il suo Rittratto | N. There was written upon on Old Pasting of this Drawing, in a good Ancient Hand, that it was | the Portrait of Baccio Bandinelli by | Martin Heimskirk; which is not unlikely, He being in | Italy in the time of Baccio, & of the Age of the Portrait; which is evidently Baccio's as ap | pears by That of Giorgio Vasari's Life of him (Baccio 1487–1559. Heimskirk 1498–1574). | It hath also been said to be of Cecchino Salviati; which may very well be too, He being ac- | tually of the School of Baccio, & of a Time that agrees (1507–1563). This name is now | on the back, & it is in his stile of Finishing.*

To the list of artists the younger Jonathan Richardson cited in the inscription quoted above, Otto Benesch added the further attribution of Melchior Lorch, but the most recent connoisseurship now agrees that the drawing is actually in the "stile of Finishing" of Francesco Salviati. Before reading the inscription, both Iris Cheney and Philip Pouncey independently identified Salviati as the draughtsman of the highly finished mannerist head. Such a bearded type not infrequently occurs in Salviati's paintings, so that it seems somewhat unlikely that it was intended as a portrait, the small mole to the left of the nose notwithstanding. In connection, however, with the old tradition that identifies the subject as Baccio Bandinelli, it may be remarked that the engraving by Giovanni Cecchi (1748–1807) after the painting in the Isabella Stewart Gardner Museum, Boston, identified as a portrait of Bandinelli, by some as a self-portrait, is inscribed *Baccio Bandinelli Scultore e Arch. Fiorentino. Fran. Salviati Pins* . . . . Such resemblance as exists between the head of the painted portrait and that of the Morgan drawing is not conclusive.

PROVENANCE: Jonathan Richardson Junior (Lugt 2170); Richard Cosway (Lugt 629); Sir Thomas Bowey (according to inscription on mount); Charles Fairfax Murray; purchased by J. Pierpont Morgan in London, 1910.

BIBLIOGRAPHY: Otto Benesch, "Eine Bildniszeichnung des Baccio Bandinelli von Melchior Lorch," *Studi Vasariani. Atti del convegno internazionale . . . Firenze 1950*, 1952, pp. 244–248, repr.

EXHIBITIONS: Baltimore, The Baltimore Museum of Art, "Bacchiacca and his Friends," 1961, no. 69, repr.

*The Pierpont Morgan Library
No. I, 6B*

103   *Design for a Fantastic Emblem*

Pen and brown ink, brown wash. 7½ × 7⅜ inches (19.1 × 18.7 cm.).

Inscribed in pen and brown ink at lower right, *Iulio Romano.*

An old inscription attributes the drawing to Giulio Romano, but the pen style is typical of Salviati, who was at least Giulio's equal in almost perversely fantastic invention. Here one of the two heads of a horse, which is precariously perched on a small base, breathes out fire that is attracting a moth. The group is surrounded by a banderole with an illegible inscription. A variant design, with a grotesque human head and an elephant in place of the horse, is in the Louvre (Inv. 12,085, as anonymous Italian).

PROVENANCE: Richard Cosway (Lugt 628).

EXHIBITIONS: Oakland, Scholz Exhibition, 1961, no. 74; Hamburg, Scholz Exhibition, 1963, no. 141, pl. 33.

Janos Scholz

Giorgio Vasari

Arezzo 1511–Florence 1574

104   *The Annunciation*

Pen and brown ink, brown wash, squared in black chalk. Diameter 5¼ inches (13.3 cm.). No watermark. Stain at right center edge.

Verso: System of circular compartments in black chalk.

A characteristic example of Vasari's draughtsmanship in its most elegant aspect, this drawing has not as yet been identified with any painted composition although the squaring indicates that the design was to have been carried a step further. It bears no relation to the *Annunciation* in the Louvre, the picture originally executed for the monks of S. Maria Novella. The system of circular compartments on the verso is perhaps a scheme for a ceiling of which the roundel of the *Annunciation* might have been a part.

PROVENANCE: Charles Fairfax Murray; purchased by J. Pierpont Morgan in London, 1910.

BIBLIOGRAPHY: Fairfax Murray, I, no. 35, repr. (as Bronzino); Arthur McComb, *Agnolo Bronzino*, Cambridge, Massachusetts, 1928, p. 152 (not Bronzino).

EXHIBITIONS: Baltimore, The Baltimore Museum of Art, "Bacchiacca and his Friends," 1961, no. 78.

*The Pierpont Morgan Library
No. I, 35*

Lelio Orsi

Novellara, probably 1511–Novellara 1587

105   *The Flight into Egypt*

Pen and brown ink, brown wash, over black chalk. 11 × 11¹⁵⁄₁₆ inches (27.9 × 30.3 cm.). Lined.

Inscribed in pen and brown ink at lower left, *Novellara Lelio Orsi*; at lower right in red ink, *13*. Inscribed on verso in pencil, *1446* and *From Dr. Chauncey's collection.*

The Flight into Egypt, showing the Holy Family fleeing into a mysterious rocky landscape, is a pleasing example of the draughtsmanship of the oddly individual Emilian mannerist who escaped mention by both Vasari and Baldinucci. There are overtones of Correggio in the types, and it is not impossible that the artist knew Dürer's woodcut of the same subject (Bartsch, VII, no. 89). Joseph is not often shown riding as he is in this drawing.

PROVENANCE: Nathaniel Hone (Lugt 2793); Dr. Chauncey (according to inscription on lining); Charles Fairfax Murray; purchased by J. Pierpont Morgan in London, 1910.

BIBLIOGRAPHY: Fairfax Murray, I, no. 51, repr.; Venturi, IX, Part 6, p. 639, fig. 384.

*The Pierpont Morgan Library
No. I, 51*

106 Design for a Façade Decoration

Pen and brown ink. 8⁵⁄₁₆ × 11¹⁄₁₆ inches (21.2 × 28.1 cm.). Two sheets joined horizontally at center.

Inscribed in pen and brown ink at lower left margin, *Iolio*.

Verso: Pen studies for the dead Christ, for architecture and drapery.

Lelio Orsi is known to have been a specialist in fresco façade painting, and he is said to have decorated many palace façades in his native Novellara. These exterior frescoes have not survived, but this drawing gives a very suggestive notion of the complexity of his ingenious schemes. Caryatids and crouching male nudes separate framed rectangular areas occupied by a loosely draped dancing female figure and at the upper right by a rocky landscape, unique in Orsi's surviving drawings, where prying wind gods watch a couple making love in a grotto. As Florence Kossoff points out, the caryatids in the scheme reappear in fragments of interior frescoes by Orsi removed from the Casino di Sopra in Novellara (repr. *Mostra di Lelio Orsi*, Reggio Emilia, 1950, nos. 18–35). A pen study by Orsi for similar caryatids is in the Seattle Art Museum.

PROVENANCE: H. Beckmann (Lugt S. 2756a).

EXHIBITIONS: Hamburg, Scholz Exhibition, 1963, no. 103, pl. 21.

Janos Scholz

Niccolò dell' Abbate

Modena 1512–France (Fontainebleau?) 1571

107 Peace

Black chalk, modeled with point of brush and white on gray prepared paper. 9¾ × 5½ inches (24.7 × 14 cm.). Irregularly cut.

The laurel-crowned figure of Peace poised triumphantly on the arms of war and raising another laurel branch aloft is a drawing of the artist's Italian period, probably executed in the 1540s when Niccolò was working in his native Modena and in Bologna, some time before his call to Fontainebleau in 1552 as the collaborator of Pri-

maticcio. A descendant of Parmigianino's Virgins of the Steccata, the figure has an almost identical counterpart in the Virgilia of the Albertina's drawing *Coriolanus Receiving His Wife and His Mother in the Volscian Camp* (Inv. 14396. Repr. O. Benesch, *Meisterzeichnungen der Albertina*, 1964, pl. 34).

EXHIBITIONS: Indianapolis, Pontormo to Greco, 1954, no. 26, repr.

Private Collection

108 Arms of Pope Julius III

Pen and brown ink, brown wash, heightened with white on paper tinted light brown. 8⁷⁄₁₆ × 10¾ inches (21.3 × 27.2 cm.). Lined.

Inscribed in pencil at lower left, *Parmigianino*.

Like No. 107 of the exhibition, the present design showing the arms of Pope Julius III is a work of Niccolò's Italian period. Julius III reigned from 1550 to 1555, so the drawing was most likely made between 1550 and 1552, the year the artist left for France. Niccolò's characteristic female types here appear as Faith and Charity flanking the escutcheon, with the triple mounts and laurel branches of the Del Monte family. Philip Pouncey was the first to identify the drawing as the work of Niccolò dell' Abbate.

PROVENANCE: Sir John Charles Robinson; Sale of a Well-known Amateur [Sir John Charles Robinson], London, Christie's, May 12–14, 1902, no. 252 (as Parmigianino); Charles Fairfax Murray; purchased by J. Pierpont Morgan in London, 1910.

The Pierpont Morgan Library
No. I, 50B

Pirro Ligorio

Naples 1513/1514–Ferrara 1583

109 Two Male Figures

Pen, yellow-brown ink, and wash, over black chalk. 8¾ × 4¹⁵⁄₁₆ inches (22.2 × 12.5 cm.).

Inscribed in pen and yellow-brown ink, presumably in the hand of the artist, on piece of paper attached to lower margin of drawing, *ERNESTUS · VI · HENRICI | XX · FILIUS* and *FRANCISCUS · II HENRICI | XX · FILIUS*; in pen and brown ink in another hand on piece of paper attached to lower margin of the above, *fratres Luneburgenses duce | obÿt 1456 | obÿt 1549.* [sic]; in pen and yellow-brown ink at right margin of sheet, *hab* . . . .

This sheet is part of a series of at least thirty-two drawings by Pirro Ligorio, each representing a pair of distinguished members of the House of Este, that once may have formed a long continuous scroll. The present drawing is unpublished, but the other sheets have been discussed by Jean Seznec (*Revue des Arts*, IV, 1954, pp. 24–26), David R. Coffin (*Art Bulletin*, XXXVII, 1955, pp. 167–185), and Parker (*Ashmolean Catalogue*, II, nos. 256–279). The drawings were probably made by Ligorio to illustrate Giovanni Battista Pigna's *Historia de' principi d'Este*, the first edition of which appeared, without the illustrations, in Ferrara in 1570. This work attempted to establish the unbroken descent of the Este family from the Roman Caius Atticus, and Ligorio's chronology is based on the genealogical tree supplied by Pigna. Ligorio's drawings were no doubt used as models for the monochrome frescoes representing two hundred notables of the Este family painted by two minor artists, Bartolomeo and Girolamo Faccini, on the four walls of the courtyard of the Este castle at Ferrara before 1577. If all the figures painted by the Faccini brothers were modeled after Pirro Ligorio's drawing, then at the rate of two figures to an architectural framework, as is the case with all the surviving drawings, more than half of Ligorio's designs have disappeared. Twenty-four of the drawings are in the Ashmolean Museum at Oxford, four in the British Museum, one in the Uffizi, and several in private collections abroad. Ligorio's designs served as models for book illustrations only much later, when thirteen of them were used for engravings illustrating a text by Antonio Cariola, *Ritratti de' ser.^mi principi d'Este Sig.^ri di Ferrara*, published in Ferrara in 1641. Pirro Ligorio, an artist and antiquarian of Neapolitan birth but active in Rome, was intermittently in the service of the Estes from 1549, when he was hired as antiquarian by Ippolito II d'Este, Cardinal of Ferrara, for whom he later designed the magnificent gardens of the Villa d'Este at Tivoli. The two figures represented in this drawing are designated by the inscriptions

below as Ernesto VI and Francesco II, sons of Enrico XX d'Este and brothers of the Duke of Lunebourg.

PROVENANCE: Purchased by the Metropolitan Museum in London, 1963.

The Metropolitan Museum of Art
Rogers Fund, 63.106

110 *Life of Virbius (Hippolytus)*

Sixteen drawings in pen and brown ink, brown and gray washes, and commentary, on twenty folios; on folio 19 an inscription in a seventeenth-century (?) hand, and in the same hand a title page reading: *Vita di Virbio | detto altrimente | Hippolito figlio di Theseo | Descritta e dissegnata | Con immitatione dell' Antico | In sedici historie | Da Pirro Ligorio Antiquario famoso | Di sua propria mano | Per seruitio del Card. d'Este Il vecchio | Che voleua farne fare vna tapezzeria d'Arazzi.* Bound in half-calf. Leaves: 12¾ × 8¾ inches (32.3 × 22.2 cm.).

Signed and dated on folio 18, *Pyrrho Ligorio Romano Meisopogniero, Novembre del M:DLXIX.*

In November 1569, the painter, architect, and antiquarian Ligorio, then in Ferrara, finished this illustrated manuscript of the life of the Greek hero Hippolytus and sent it to Rome to his patron Cardinal Ippolito II d'Este with an apology for the delay in its completion. He signed it, as was his custom, *Pyrrho Ligorio Romano Meisopogniero*, that is, "hater of the wicked." According to the later title page, which was probably added in the seventeenth century, the Cardinal wished to have tapestries made from these drawings of the career of his legendary namesake. Coffin points out that such tapestries most likely would have been meant for the Villa d'Este at Tivoli, where Ligorio had been involved at intervals in the Cardinal's establishment of a splendid country residence and gardens. Girolamo Muziano, Federico Zuccaro, and Giovanni de' Vecchi, all represented in the present exhibition, also worked for the Cardinal at Tivoli.

Seventeenth-century copies of the Morgan manuscript are found in the Bibliothèque de l'Arsenal, Paris (Ms. Ital. 8529), and the Biblioteca Estense, Modena.

Ligorio's composition of the Birth of Hippolytus, to which the manuscript is opened, displays a mixture of the iconography of the Birth of the

Virgin and the representation of the Birth of Dionysus.

PROVENANCE: Francesco Villamena (according to the title page); Giuseppe Cavalieri; purchased by J. Pierpont Morgan, 1909.

BIBLIOGRAPHY: *Catalogue des livres composant la Bibliothèque de M. Giuseppe Cavalieri in Ferrara*, Florence, 1908, p. 5, no. xii; Thieme-Becker, XXIII, p. 219; S. de Ricci and W. J. Wilson, *Census of Medieval and Renaissance Manuscripts in the United States and Canada*, II, New York, 1937, p. 1436, no. 376; David R. Coffin, *The Villa d'Este at Tivoli*, Princeton, 1960, pp. 69–77; 151–159, figs. 90–105 (with transcription of text and fully illustrated).

The Pierpont Morgan Library
M.A. 542

Guglielmo della Porta

Porlezza 1514/1515–Rome 1577

111   *The Banquet of the Gods*

Pen and brown ink, over traces of black chalk. 4¹³⁄₁₆ × 6⅝ inches (12.2 × 16.8 cm.). Repairs at top left and two lower corners; left margin irregular. Lined.

Study for one of a series of sixteen plaques representing scenes from Ovid's *Metamorphoses,* originally cast in bronze for della Porta by Cobaert. The Metropolitan Museum possesses a fine version of this particular scene in repoussé gold backed with lapis lazuli (exhibited on this occasion close to the drawing). Guglielmo's spidery draughtsmanship, which owes much to Perino del Vaga with whom he collaborated in Genoa and Rome, is well documented in sketchbooks at Düsseldorf, recently published in facsimile (Gramberg, *Düsseldorfer Skizzenbücher*). In addition to No. 112 below, two further designs for the *Metamorphoses* plaques are in the collection of Erich Bier in Copenhagen. These drawings represent the Flaying of Marsyas and the Judgment of Paris.

PROVENANCE: Mark formerly associated with Pierre Crozat (Lugt S. 474); John F. Keane; sale, London, Sotheby's, May 21, 1963, no. 55; purchased by the Metropolitan Museum in London, 1963.

The Metropolitan Museum of Art
Rogers Fund, 63.103.3

112   *The Fall of the Giants*

Pen and brown ink and leadpoint. 7⅛ × 10³⁄₁₆ inches

(17.8 × 26 cm.). Watermark: rampant lion holding a shield. Stained and foxed.

Inscribed on verso in pen and brown ink, *tre varie*.

Verso: Pen and brown ink study of a cup, and of two figures.

Like No. 111 of the exhibition, this drawing is a study for one of the Ovid plaques of which a complete series of sixteen in bronze exists only in the Kunsthistorisches Museum at Vienna. The two drawings now in New York, which were once together in the same collection (Lugt S. 474), are among the few surviving sketches that are directly preparatory for the plaques. There is, however, a sketch of a subject from the *Metamorphoses* in the third Düsseldorf sketchbook (Gramberg, *Düsseldorfer Skizzenbücher*, no. 180). Also in this third sketchbook is the draft of a letter addressed by Guglielmo to Giovannantonio Dosio on May 24, 1574, in which he mentions that he is sending a "schizzo della fulminatione delli giganti" to be given to Cavaliere Gaddi. Quite possibly the Morgan drawing is that dispatched to Niccolò Gaddi, a Florentine collector to whom Guglielmo leased his house in the Via Giulia, Rome, in 1575. The bronze plaque of this subject in the Metropolitan Museum is the work of the artist's natural son, Fidia.

Gramberg in his article in the Hamburg *Jahrbuch* connects the sketches on the verso of the Morgan sheet with silver-gilt tableware executed by Antonio Gentile da Faenza.

PROVENANCE: Mark formerly associated with Pierre Crozat (Lugt S. 474); Jonathan Richardson Senior (Lugt 2183); John Barnard (Lugt 1419); Thomas Lawrence (Lugt 2445); Charles Fairfax Murray; purchased by J. Pierpont Morgan in London, 1910.

BIBLIOGRAPHY: Fairfax Murray, I, no. 33, repr. (as Cellini); Ulrich Middeldorf, "Two Wax Reliefs by Guglielmo della Porta," *Art Bulletin*, XVII, 1935, p. 95, n. 12, fig. 6; Maria Gibellino Krasceninnicowa, *Guglielmo della Porta*, Rome, 1944, p. 55; Ulrich Middeldorf and Oswald Goetz, *Medals and Plaquettes from the Sigmund Morgenroth Collection*, Chicago, 1944, under no. 320; Werner Gramberg, "Guglielmo della Porta, Coppe Fiammingo und Antonio Gentile da Faenza," *Jahrbuch der Hamburger Kunstsammlungen*, V, 1960, pp. 32–34, 48, figs. 1, 18; Gramberg, *Düsseldorfer Skizzenbücher*, pp. 32, 100, 104.

EXHIBITIONS: Buffalo, Master Drawings, 1935, no. 26, repr.; New York, Morgan Library, World's Fair, 1939, no. 72; 1940, no. 90; Indianapolis, Pontormo to Greco, 1954, no. 36, repr.

Jacopo da Ponte, called Jacopo Bassano

Bassano 1517/1518–1592

113 *Head of a Bearded Old Man*

Black, brown, red, and white chalk. 10¾ × 7⅞ inches (27.3 × 18.7 cm.).

Inscribed in pen and brown ink at lower right, *Bassano*.

A powerful, characteristic example of Jacopo Bassano's portraiture. This very painterly use of colored chalks to model form was something of a specialty in Jacopo's studio.

PROVENANCE: Borghese Collection, Rome (?) (pen inscription on verso, *B.B. n.° 58*, in a hand similar to Lugt S. 2103a); Maurice Marignane (Lugt 1872); Hubert Marignane (Lugt S. 1343a).

EXHIBITIONS: Oakland, Scholz Exhibition, 1959, no. 5, repr.; New York, Seiferheld Gallery, "Bassano Drawings," 1961, no. 3, repr.; Hamburg, Scholz Exhibition, 1963, no. 10; New Haven, Scholz Exhibition, 1964, no. 25.

Janos Scholz

Jacopo Robusti, called Tintoretto

Venice 1518–Venice 1594

114 *Head of the Emperor Vitellius*

Charcoal and white chalk on gray paper. 13⁷⁄₁₆ × 9¹³⁄₁₆ inches (33.2 × 25 cm.). Lined.

A good dozen of the surviving drawings after antique models by Tintoretto and his atelier are studies of the bull-necked Roman Emperor Vitellius. The present monumental head may be compared with examples of varying quality preserved in the British Museum (five drawings), the Uffizi, the Library of Christ Church, the Munich Graphische Sammlung, the École des Beaux-Arts, Paris, the Louvre, the Koenigs Collection in the Museum Boymans-van Beuningen, and the Richard Sterba Collection, Grosse Pointe Park, Michigan.

Carlo Ridolfi, among others of Tintoretto's biographers, reports that the artist drew from casts in his studio at night, continuously experimenting with lighting and unusual points of view. Tintoretto's cast of Vitellius is presumed to have been made from the Roman portrait head of the Emperor, which was included in the gift of ancient sculpture presented to the city of Venice by Cardinal Domenico Grimani in 1523 and still is preserved in the city's Archaeological Museum. The Morgan *Vitellius* differs from other versions in its vivification of the plastic model. The eyes are indicated and the head endowed with a nobility not inherent in the sculpture, nor for that matter, in the historical personage himself. Indolent and self-indulgent, especially in eating and drinking, Vitellius survived as emperor only from January 2 to December 22, A. D. 69, when he was assassinated by the forces of Vespasian.

PROVENANCE: Purchased by the Pierpont Morgan Library in London, 1959.

BIBLIOGRAPHY: Morgan Library, *Tenth Fellows Report, 1960*, pp. 50–51, repr.

115 *Man Climbing into a Boat*

Charcoal, squared; ruled border in brown ink. 8 × 12¼ inches (20.2 × 31.1 cm.). Watermark: shield surmounted by a star.

Inscribed in pen and brown ink in an old (eighteenth-century) hand at lower right, and also on verso, *G. Tintoretto*.

Verso: Tracing and separate study of the same figure, in charcoal.

A preparatory study, in reverse, for the figure of a Venetian soldier who has fallen into the water in the *Battle of the River Adige at Legnano* (repr. Hans Tietze, *Tintoretto*, London, 1948, pl. 222), the painting representing Ludovico Gonzaga's defeat of the Venetians in 1439. The picture, executed in 1579 when the artist was in his sixties, is one of a series of eight commemorating the exploits of the Gonzagas, originally hanging in the Palazzo Ducale at Mantua but now in the Alte Pinakothek at Munich.

As Walter Vitzthum noted in the Toronto catalogue, the Morgan drawing has on occasion been reproduced in the vertical orientation that the placement of Sir Joshua Reynolds's stamp obviously indicated was thought correct in his day. The drawing was reproduced in its proper horizontality when E. Tietze-Conrat first identified the subject in 1936.

PROVENANCE: Sir Joshua Reynolds (Lugt 2364); Charles Fairfax Murray; purchased by J. Pierpont Morgan in London, 1910.

BIBLIOGRAPHY: Fairfax Murray, IV, no. 76, repr.; E. Tietze-Conrat, "Echte und unechte Tintorettozeichnungen," *Die Graphischen Künste*, n. s. I, 1936, pp. 90–91, fig. 3; Charles de Tolnay, *History and Techniques of Old Master Drawings*, New York, 1943, p. 127, no. 133, pl. 133; Tietze, *Venetian Drawings*, no. 1727.

EXHIBITIONS: Toledo, Venetian Painting, 1940, no. 93; Northampton, Smith College, Italian Drawings, 1941, no. 40; Worcester, Fiftieth Anniversary Exhibition, 1948, no. 37; Toronto, Art Gallery of Toronto, "Titian, Tintoretto, Paolo Veronese," 1960, no. 17.

The Pierpont Morgan Library
No. IV, 76

Andrea Meldolla, called Schiavone

Zara 1522–Venice 1563

116 *Psyche Presented to the Gods*

Pen and brown ink, brown wash, heightened with white, over traces of black chalk, on brown washed paper. 14⅝ × 23⅝ inches (37.4 × 60 cm.). Lined.

The composition of this highly pictorial drawing, exceptional in its dimensions, derives from Raphael's representation of the same subject in a fresco at the Farnesina, but the graceful, elongated physical types reveal the dominant influence of Parmigianino. Schiavone's own contribution is the masterful play of broad accents of light and shade over the surface of the friezelike group.

PROVENANCE: C. R. Rudolf (Lugt S. 2811b); Rudolf sale, London, Sotheby's, May 21, 1963, no. 11, repr., bought by the Metropolitan Museum.

EXHIBITIONS: London, Arts Council, "Old Master Drawings from the Collection of Mr. C. R. Rudolf," 1962, no. 62, pl. 3.

The Metropolitan Museum of Art
Rogers Fund, 63.93

Paolo Farinato

Verona 1524–Verona 1606

117 *Verona*

Pen and dark brown ink, brown wash, heightened with white on dark yellow prepared paper. 16¹¹⁄₁₆ × 14⅝ inches (42.4 × 37.2 cm.). Small repairs at margins, some breaks, two small stains at upper center. Lined.

Signed at the lower right with the artist's device of a snail and dated *A.D.M.D./LVIII.*

In his catalogue of the Italian drawings at Windsor Castle, where there is an important group of Farinato drawings, Popham speculates that the artist may have made drawings for sale or gift. This highly finished sheet, which is dated and bears at the lower right the snail that Farinato sometimes used as a signature on drawings as well as paintings, would have been an effective presentation piece and all the more interesting in that Verona was the artist's native city.

The city with the *colle di San Pietro* rising above the Adige River is seen in the background to the right, and Verona's famous Roman amphitheatre is barely glimpsed at the far left. The precise meaning of the scene, however, is not clear. The seated woman with the crown might conceivably be interpreted as a personification of Venice, since she wears on her breast that city's emblem of the winged lion of St. Mark. If so, the infant to whom the lion displays the cross of Verona might logically be regarded as personifying Verona, which was under the government of the Venetians. The small baptizing angels are antithetical to the pagan river god shouldering the cask and bale of the prosperous commerce of the Adige River. The significance here of the ox, usually the emblem of St. Luke, is yet to be explained; were it a bull, some reference to Europa might be involved.

PROVENANCE: Charles Fairfax Murray; purchased by J. Pierpont Morgan in London, 1910.

BIBLIOGRAPHY: Fairfax Murray, I, no. 87, repr.; Thieme-Becker, XI, p. 273.

The Pierpont Morgan Library
No. I, 87

118 Saints Adoring the Virgin and Child

Pen and brown ink, brown wash, over black chalk, heightened with white, on blue paper. 16⅜ × 11⅛ inches (41.6 × 28.3 cm.). Lined.

Inscribed in pen and brown ink with the name of each saint, except Jerome, S. francescho, S. Ludovicho, S. Lanardo, S. isepo, S. diego, S. inoforio.

This late work of the prolific Veronese master exists in another version in the Louvre (Inv. 4836, 42 × 28 cm.), which is dated July 6, 1596. The representation of S. Diego was then still timely, as the Spanish saint had been canonized only eight years before, in 1588.

PROVENANCE: Sir John Charles Robinson (Lugt 1433); Charles Fairfax Murray; purchased by J. Pierpont Morgan in London, 1910.

The Pierpont Morgan Library
No. IV, 79B

Federico Barocci

Urbino 1526–Urbino 1612

119 Studies of Heads and Hands

Black chalk, heightened with white and a little red chalk, on blue paper. 11 × 16¼ inches (28 × 41.3 cm.). Lower right corner replaced.

These heads and hands are studies for the figure of the Apostle seated third from the right of Christ in a large representation of the Last Supper, painted by Barocci for the Chapel of the Blessed Sacrament in the Duomo at Urbino (repr. Venturi, IX, Part 7, p. 944, fig. 529). This late work of the artist, dating from 1592–1599, was paid for by contributions from Francesco Maria II della Rovere, duke of Urbino. Olsen lists more than fifty drawings for the *Last Supper*, and these testify to the care with which Barocci prepared his canvases and to his mastery of bold, broad modeling in black and white chalk.

PROVENANCE: The Earls Spencer (Lugt 1530); Spencer sale, London, June 10, 1811, no. 22; Lionel Lucas (Lugt S. 1733a); Lucas sale, London, Christie's, December 9, 1949, no. 54; purchased by the Metropolitan Museum in London, 1950.

BIBLIOGRAPHY: Marilyn Aronberg Lavin, "A Late Work by Barocci," *Metropolitan Museum of Art Bulletin*, May

1955, pp. 267–268, repr. p. 271; Harald Olsen, *Federico Barocci, A Critical Study in Italian Cinquecento Painting* ("Figura," no. 6), Stockholm, 1955, p. 158; Harald Olsen, *Federico Barocci*, Copenhagen, 1962, pp. 82, 203, pl. 92a; Bean, *100 European Drawings*, no. 24, repr.

The Metropolitan Museum of Art
Rogers Fund, 50.143

Luca Cambiaso

Moneglia 1527–Madrid 1585

120 The Martyrdom of St. Sebastian

Pen and brown ink, brown wash, over traces of black chalk. 22⅛ × 16⅜ inches (56.2 × 41.7 cm.) (sight). Horizontal crease at center. Repairs at corners and margins.

This large-scale example of Cambiaso's bravura draughtsmanship is placed early in the artist's career by Bertina Suida Manning, who points out that a weak copy of the sheet is in the Victoria and Albert Museum (Dyce 338).

PROVENANCE: Benjamin West (his monogram on verso).

BIBLIOGRAPHY: Bertina Suida Manning and William Suida, *Luca Cambiaso, la vita e le opere*, Milan, 1958, p. 190, fig. 57.

EXHIBITIONS: Indianapolis, Pontormo to Greco, 1954, no. 47, repr.; Detroit, Drawings of the Italian Renaissance, 1960, no. 43, repr.; Dayton/Sarasota/Hartford, "Genoese Masters," 1962–1963, no. 67, repr.; New York, Finch College Museum of Art, "Genoese Painters," 1964–1965, no. 12, repr.

Robert and Bertina Suida Manning

Pellegrino Tibaldi

Puria di Valsolda 1527–Milan 1596

121 Seated Figure

Red chalk, squared. 18¾ × 13⅜ inches (47.6 × 34 cm.). Watermark: fleur-de-lis in a circle (compare Briquet 6895). Old fold across center.

Inscribed in red chalk on a plaque held by a putto, *AMOR DEI*. Inscribed on verso in pen and black ink at upper center, *Michel Angli⁰ Bona Rotta*; in red chalk just below, *Michel Angi⁰ B. F. / Roma*. Various numbers in black chalk at lower right.

Squared as it is for enlargement or transfer, it might have been anticipated that this full-bodied figure was preparatory for one of the decorative seated nudes in the frescoes (about 1554) of the Palazzo Poggi at Bologna, which so patently pay homage to Michelangelo's Sistine sibyls and *ignudi*. However, only segments of the figure appear in the paintings. The upper half of the figure is clearly related to the head and shoulders of Ino in the scene where the sea goddess rescues Ulysses by giving him her scarf to buoy him up (Giuliano Briganti, *Il Manierismo e Pellegrino Tibaldi*, Rome, 1945, fig. 126); the legs are similar to those of the decorative figure illustrated by Briganti as fig. 119.

Prior to the recognition of the drawing as Tibaldi's by the authorities at the British Museum some years ago, it was ascribed to Daniele da Volterra, under whom Tibaldi worked in the Della Rovere Chapel in S. Trinità dei Monti at Rome. A comparable highly finished drawing by Tibaldi, though in black rather than red chalk, was published by J. A. Gere in the *British Museum Quarterly*, XXVI, nos. 1–2, 1962, pp. 40–41, pl. xxiv.

PROVENANCE: Edward Bouverie (Lugt 325); Charles Fairfax Murray; purchased by J. Pierpont Morgan in London, 1910.

BIBLIOGRAPHY: Fairfax Murray, IV, no. 27, repr. (as Daniele da Volterra).

EXHIBITIONS: Cambridge, Fogg Art Museum, Anxiety and Elegance, 1962, no. 37.

The Pierpont Morgan Library
No. IV, 27

122 *St. John the Baptist Preaching*

Pen and brown ink, brown wash. 9⅜ × 12¾ inches (23.8 × 32.4 cm.).

On the side walls of the Poggi Chapel in S. Giacomo Maggiore at Bologna, Tibaldi painted two scenes from the life of the Baptist. These frescoes probably date from the mid-1550s, while the altarpiece of the chapel, left unfinished by Tibaldi, was completed by Prospero Fontana in 1561. The present drawing, as Philip Pouncey has pointed out, is Tibaldi's free sketch for the lower half of the wall fresco representing the Baptist preaching (repr. Giuliano Briganti, *Il Manierismo e Pellegrino Tibaldi*, Rome, 1945, fig. 134).

PROVENANCE: Sir Robert Witt, London; C. R. Rudolf

(Lugt S. 2811b); Rudolf sale, London, Sotheby's, May 21, 1963, no. 12, repr.

BIBLIOGRAPHY: John Gere, "Drawings from the Rudolf Collection," *Burlington Magazine*, CIV, 1962, p. 88, fig. 40.

EXHIBITIONS: London, Arts Council, "Old Master Drawings from the Collection of Mr. C. R. Rudolf," 1962, no. 65, pl. 8.

Walter C. Baker

Girolamo Muziano
Acquafredda near Brescia 1528–Rome 1592

123 *The Arrest of Christ*

Black chalk, heightened with white, on gray-green paper; squared in red chalk. 9⁵⁄₁₆ × 9⁹⁄₁₆ inches (23.6 × 24.3 cm.).

Inscribed in pen and brown ink at lower left, *P vago*; at lower right, *60 R.*

A very similar figure of Christ, represented frontally in gracefully falling drapery but with head turned to the right in profile, in a pose very characteristic of Muziano, appears in one of the artist's principal altarpieces, *The Consignment of the Keys to St. Peter*, in S. Maria degli Angeli, Rome (repr. Hermann Voss, *Die Malerei der Spätrenaissance in Rom und Florenz*, II, Berlin, 1920, p. 563, fig. 226). The very convincing attribution of the drawing to Muziano is due to Philip Pouncey.

Janos Scholz

124 *Seated Draped Male Figure*

Red chalk. 12¾ × 9¼ inches (32.4 × 23.5 cm.). Repairs at upper left corner.

Inscribed in pen and brown ink at lower right, *Mutiano*.

A typical example of the figure drawings of Muziano, who was partial to such massive figures weighed down by rich drapery. The Louvre possesses a related red chalk drawing (repr. Hermann Voss, *Zeichnungen der italienischer Spätrenaissance*, Munich, 1928, no. 24).

PROVENANCE: Brandegee Family, Brookline, Massachusetts.

EXHIBITIONS: Hamburg, Scholz Exhibition, 1963, no. 102, pl. 51; New Haven, Scholz Exhibition, 1964, no. 42.

Janos Scholz

Paolo Caliari, called Paolo Veronese

Verona about 1528–Venice 1588

125 Christ Preaching in the Temple

Pen and brown ink. 3 1/16 × 6 7/8 inches (7.8 × 17.4 cm.).

Rapid pen study in which Veronese is concerned with the grouping and the stance of figures in an early picture representing *Christ Preaching in the Temple*, now in the Prado at Madrid (repr. Fiocco, *Veronese*, 1928, pl. x). The left half of the drawing, with the youthful Christ seated on a raised platform, corresponds in general arrangement to that section of the picture; in the right half there are a number of variant solutions for the placement of the figures.

PROVENANCE: Jonathan Richardson Senior (Lugt 2183).

BIBLIOGRAPHY: Hans Tietze, "Nuovi disegni veneti del cinquecento in collezioni americane," *Arte Veneta*, II, 1948, p. 60, fig. 71.

S. Schwarz Collection

126 Studies for a Finding of Moses

Pen and brown ink, brown wash. 6 3/4 × 7 5/16 inches (17.1 × 18.6 cm.). Lined.

None of this sheet's trial groupings of the characters in the scene of the discovery of the infant Moses by Pharaoh's daughter corresponds specifically to Veronese's small painting of the subject in the Prado (Fiocco, *Veronese*, 1934, pl. CLXXXVII), but the group of three figures at the left, where Pharaoh's daughter is shown with her hands on her hips, is near enough to have been a germinal idea for the painting. The rapid notation of the cluster of buildings on a river, crowded in at the top of the sheet, could conceivably have expanded into the city in the middle distance of the painted composition. The female nudes at the lower right might indicate that the artist at one point contemplated showing Pharaoh's daughter bathing, in accordance with the Biblical text that "she came down to wash herself at the river" (Exodus 2:5). The Prado picture is usually dated about 1570, a date also acceptable for the drawing.

A second sheet of quite different ideas for another *Finding of Moses* was formerly in the possession of Tancred Borenius in London (Tietze, no. 2099).

PROVENANCE: Thomas Hudson (Lugt 2432); Sir Joshua Reynolds (Lugt 2364); Earl of Aylesford (Lugt 58); Charles Fairfax Murray; purchased by J. Pierpont Morgan in London, 1910.

BIBLIOGRAPHY: Fairfax Murray, IV, no. 81, repr. (also reproduced on a smaller scale in I, no. 90); Tancred Borenius, "A Group of Drawings by Paul Veronese," *Burlington Magazine*, XXXVIII, 1921, p. 54; Detlev F. von Hadeln, *Venezianische Zeichnungen der Spätrenaissance*, Berlin, 1926, p. 27; Percy H. Osmond, *Paolo Veronese, His Career and Work*, London, 1927, p. 100; Fiocco, *Veronese*, 1928, p. 209; Fiocco, *Veronese*, 1934, p. 130; Tietze, *Venetian Drawings*, no. 2121, pl. CLXI, 3; Lisa Oehler, "Eine Gruppe von Veronese-Zeichnungen in Berlin und Kassel," *Berliner Museen, Berichte aus den Ehem. Preussischen Kunstsammlungen*, n. s. III, 1953, p. 31; Moskowitz, ed., *Great Drawings*, I, pl. 233.

EXHIBITIONS: Toledo, Venetian Painting, 1940, no. 97; Worcester, Fiftieth Anniversary Exhibition, 1948, no. 38; Toronto, Art Gallery of Toronto, "Titian, Tintoretto, Paolo Veronese," 1960, no. 48, repr.; Hartford, Morgan Treasures, 1960, no. 70.

*The Pierpont Morgan Library
No. IV, 81*

127 Studies for Venice Receiving Homage and for a Baptism of Christ
Verso: *Venice Receiving Homage*

Pen and brown ink, brown and gray wash. 8 × 11 5/16 inches (20.3 × 28.8 cm.). Vertical crease at center.

Inscribed in the artist's hand in pen and brown ink on recto and verso; in pen and brown ink in another hand at lower center of verso, *P. Ver^{se} 7. 2.*

Byam Shaw, who first published this drawing, thus transcribed the inscriptions in the artist's hand, on the recto, *Vene[z]ia che seli apresenta Tributi [dalle?] provincie città castele p[er] il buon governo ed [?] dar grazie* (Venice receiving tribute from the provinces, cities and fortresses, in gratitude for good government); on verso, *Primo nel fianco a la banda [?] destra del Coligio* (First on the flank on the right side of the Collegio). With the exception of the design for a Baptism of Christ at upper left of recto, all the sketches seem related to the composition described in the longer inscription, i.e., Venice Receiving Homage. Venice is enthroned between female figures; soldiers carry booty, and enchained prisoners cower. The second inscription refers to the Sala del Collegio in the Doge's Palace in Venice. Byam Shaw has pointed out that there are certain compositional similarities between the groups sketched here by Veronese and that painter's *Venice Enthroned between Justice and Peace*, datable 1576–1577, one of the central compartments of the ceiling of the Sala del Collegio (repr. Fiocco, *Veronese*, 1928, pl. LXXV); but the subjects are not the same. On the other hand, Venice Receiving the Homage of Brescia, Udine, Padua, and Verona is represented in a picture by Palma Giovane, in the adjacent Sala del Senato, that includes motifs adumbrated in these Veronese sketches. The Tietzes suggested that Veronese may have competed for the commission that was allotted to Palma Giovane.

PROVENANCE: Sir Peter Lely (Lugt 2092); Sutton Palmer; C. R. Rudolf (Lugt S. 2811b).

BIBLIOGRAPHY: J. Byam Shaw, *Old Master Drawings*, X, 1935, no. 38, pp. 22–24, pl. 23 (recto), pl. 24 (verso); Tietze, *Venetian Drawings*, no. 2106, pl. CLV, 2 (recto).

Private Collection

128 *Studies for an Assumption of the Virgin and for an Adoration*

Pen and brown ink, brown wash, and a few strokes of red chalk, on paper tinted red. 8½ × 8¼ inches (21.7 × 21 cm.). Lined.

Inscribed in pencil at lower right, *paolo*.

The artist swiftly set down ideas for two different subjects on this sheet. The upper two-thirds is given over to studies for a lofty, spiraling composition of an Assumption of the Virgin; the remaining section plots a long horizontal scene, presumably an Adoration of the Shepherds, where the Virgin exhibits the Child to the figures kneeling on the left.

The Tietzes associated the Assumption studies with the late painting of the subject (about 1580 according to Osmond, p. 115) formerly in S. Maria Maggiore, now in the Galleria dell' Accademia, Venice (Fiocco, *Veronese*, 1934, pl. CLXXXIIIa). There the Virgin appears much as indicated in the figure sketched in the upper center of the drawing,

but the lower part of the composition is much simplified and not noticeably similar, with the possible exception of the two figures kneeling before the sarcophagus. The Tietzes' attempt to link the drawing with the *Assumption* in the Chapel of the Rosary, SS. Giovanni e Paolo, Venice (Fiocco, *Veronese*, 1934, pl. CLXIX b), on the solitary evidence of the figure with the upraised arm, would seem to be somewhat tenuous. They also suggested an unlikely connection between the lower part of the drawing and the *Adoration of the Shepherds* in SS. Giovanni e Paolo, a picture Osmond (p. 117) regarded as dubious (Venice, *Mostra di Paolo Veronese*, 1939, no. 48, repr.). A more pertinent comparison with the group of the Holy Family and the two animals of the drawing is offered by the right half of the *Adoration of the Magi*, National Gallery, London, a painting dated 1573.

PROVENANCE: Luigi Grassi (Lugt S. 1171b); sale, under the initials G. L. [Grassi], London, Sotheby's, May 13, 1924.

BIBLIOGRAPHY: Detlev F. von Hadeln, *Venezianische Zeichnungen der Spätrenaissance*, Berlin, 1926, p. 27; Percy H. Osmond, *Paolo Veronese, His Career and Work*, London, 1927, p. 101; Tietze, *Venetian Drawings*, no. 2124, pl. CLIV, 1.

EXHIBITIONS: Philadelphia, Masterpieces of Drawing, 1950–1951, no. 43, repr.

Robert Lehman

129 *Allegory of the Redemption of the World*

Pen and black ink, gray wash, heightened with white, on gray washed paper. 24⅛ × 16⁹⁄₁₆ inches (61.4 × 42.1 cm.). Horizontal addition at lower margin of original sheet, where drawing is continued in the artist's hand. Lined.

This large and essentially pictorial drawing is part of a group of highly finished sheets, some of which were described by the Venetian historian Carlo Ridolfi when they were in the Muselli Collection in Verona in the first half of the seventeenth century. Though they have the appearance of small paintings in grisaille used as *modelli*, none corresponds to surviving pictures by the artist, and their function in the artist's workshop is uncertain. The Tietzes identified three of these drawings, two in the Louvre, and one in the Staedel Institute at

Frankfort-on-the-Main (Tietze, *Venetian Drawings*, nos. 2131, 2135, 2066, respectively). A further example is in the Albertina (Otto Benesch, *Disegni veneti dell' Albertina di Vienna*, Cini Foundation, Venice, 1961, no. 43, repr.). No. 130 of the present exhibition is specifically described by Ridolfi, who records the inscription still visible on the verso of the sheet.

The present drawing, only recently rediscovered, was pasted on to a heavy mount sometime in the eighteenth century, but Jonathan Richardson Junior, who once owned the sheet, inscribed on the back of this mount an English translation of the now invisible inscription fully describing the complex subject matter. It begins: *This Divine Poetry represents the Final Completion of the Great and Sublime Mystery of the Redemption of the World: Foretold, in various Manners & Distant Times, by the Prophets & Sibyls & in its Due Time Fully Accomplish'd by the Virgin Mary's presenting y First Author of Original Sin to the glorious Redeemer, her Son,* .... Richardson has added that *the Prophets are plac'd Above and near their High Inspirers . . . while the Sibyl, whose Prophecies were by Compulsion, without Their being let in to the Knowledge and Tendency of their own high Illuminations, are only attentive to one another, Below.*

PROVENANCE: Cristoforo and Francesco Muselli, Verona (?); Sir Peter Lely (Lugt 2093); Jonathan Richardson Junior (Lugt 2170); Norblin *fils*, Paris; Norblin *fils* sale, Paris, January 30, 1863, no. 12; purchased by the Metropolitan Museum in New York, 1961.

BIBLIOGRAPHY: J. Bean, *Metropolitan Museum of Art Bulletin*, January 1962, repr. p. 164, fig. 8; Bean, *100 European Drawings*, no. 25, repr.

The Metropolitan Museum of Art
Rogers Fund, 61.203

130   Madonna and Child with St. Anne and a Group of Angels

Pen and black ink, gray wash, heightened with white, on gray washed paper. 13³⁄₁₆ × 15⅝ inches (33.5 × 39.1 cm.). Vertical creases at center and right.

Long inscription in pen and brown ink on verso beginning, *Pittura Quinta | Io ne ho fatto una p[er] la mia camera . . . una parte del quadro è maria vergine; a sedere co[n] un libro*

inan . . . (continues for seven lines with a full description of the composition).

See No. 129 above.

PROVENANCE: Cristoforo and Francesco Muselli, Verona; Pierre Crozat; Crozat sale, Paris, April 10–May 10, 1741, p. 73, no. 680; Count Carl Gustav Tessin; Count Nils Barck (Lugt 1959).

BIBLIOGRAPHY: Carlo Ridolfi, *Le Maraviglie dell' Arte*, I, Venice, 1648, p. 307; Charles Blanc, *Le Trésor de la curiosité tiré de catalogues de vente*, I, Paris, 1857, p. 26; Pietro Caliari, *Paolo Veronese*, Rome, 1888, pp. 234–235.

EXHIBITIONS: New York, Columbia Benefit Exhibition, 1959, no. 17a, pl. XXXIV.

John Mooney

131   Head of a Negro

Black chalk on brown paper. 7⅞ × 6⅞ inches (20 × 17.5 cm.). Scattered oil stains.

Undeciphered inscription at lower right.

The Tietzes rendered a minority opinion in their rejection of the Lehman drawing and two other studies of Negro subjects (Tietze, A 2109 and A 2133) as works by Veronese. Other critics, like Borenius and Von Hadeln, followed by Osmond and Fiocco, have been unanimous in their acceptance of the New York head, which brings to mind the elegantly garbed Negro boys and men who move among Veronese's secular and religious spectacles. Compare, for example, the profile of the attendant in the Prado *Finding of Moses*. The lifted head and the upward gaze combined with the expression of worshipful awe would be appropriate for the Balthasar in an Adoration of the Magi.

PROVENANCE: Richard Cosway; Charles Fairfax Murray; A. G. B. Russell (Lugt S. 2770a).

BIBLIOGRAPHY: Tancred Borenius, "Drawings in the Collection of Mr. Archibald G. B. Russell," *Connoisseur*, LXVI, 1923, p. 10, repr.; Detlev F. von Hadeln, *Venezianische Zeichnungen der Spätrenaissance*, Berlin, 1926, p. 31, pl. 52; Percy H. Osmond, *Paolo Veronese, His Career and Work*, London, 1927, p. 104; Fiocco, *Veronese*, 1928, p. 142; Fiocco, *Veronese*, 1934, p. 129; Tietze, *Venetian Drawings*, no. A 2108, pl. CXCVI, I.

EXHIBITIONS: London, Royal Academy, Italian Art, 1930: commemorative drawings catalogue, 1931, no. 285, pl. CCXL; Paris, Lehman Collection, 1957, no. 130; Cincinnati, Lehman Collection, 1959, no. 224, repr.

Robert Lehman

Bartolomeo Passarotti

Bologna 1529–Bologna 1592

132 *An Angel*

Pen and brown ink. 16¾ × 10⅛ inches (42.5 × 25.7 cm.). Upper corners replaced.

Inscribed in pen and brown ink at lower right, *Bartholomeo Passarotto.*

A typical and quite monumental example of Passarotti's style as a draughtsman. His bold but coarse and synthetic crosshatching is ultimately derived from Michelangelo; indeed, Passarotti's drawings were often hopefully attributed to Michelangelo by collectors in the past.

PROVENANCE: Jan Pietersz. Zoomer (Lugt 1511); purchased by the Metropolitan Museum in London, 1964.

EXHIBITIONS: London, P. & D. Colnaghi, "Exhibition of Old Master Drawings," 1964, no. 11.

The Metropolitan Museum of Art
Rogers Fund, 64.197.1

Taddeo Zuccaro

Sant' Angelo in Vado 1529–Rome 1566

133 *Studies of Flying Figures*

Pen and brown ink, brown wash, heightened with white, on blue paper. 8¹¹⁄₁₆ × 11³⁄₁₆ inches (22 × 28.5 cm.).

The attribution of this drawing to Taddeo Zuccaro is due to J. A. Gere, who dates it in the early 1550s. Stylistic evidence was the basis for the attribution, which Gere was later able to confirm by pointing out that these flying figures are studies for angels that appear in the upper part of a drawing by Taddeo at Hamburg representing the Rest on the Flight into Egypt. The Hamburg sheet has been exhibited as the work of Federico Zuccaro, but is undoubtedly by Taddeo (repr. Hamburg, Kunsthalle, *Italienische Zeichnungen 1500–1800*, 1957, no. 102, pl. 17).

PROVENANCE: Jonathan Richardson Senior (Lugt 2183).

Mrs. Richard Krautheimer

134 *Studies of Nymphs Bathing in a Pool*
Verso: *Studies of Nymphs Bathing*

Pen and brown ink, brown wash. 10¾ × 8³⁄₁₆ inches (27.2 × 20.7 cm.). Watermark: close to Briquet 7106.

Inscribed on verso in pencil at upper margin, *Ecole Italienne 16ᵉ siècle*; illegible cipher in pen and brown ink at upper right corner.

The circular form of the composition studied by Taddeo on the recto and verso of this sheet naturally suggests that it may have been a design for maiolica, but the only series of such designs that the artist is recorded as having made represent episodes from Roman history (see J. A. Gere, "Taddeo Zuccaro as a Designer of Maiolica," *Burlington Magazine*, CV, 1963, pp. 306–315). It should be noted, however, that circular compositions occur at Caprarola in those rooms decorated under Taddeo's supervision. In one of these, the Sala dei Lanifici, there is a roundel with nymphs bathing at a fountain, much less elaborate than the present design. The drawing came to the Metropolitan Museum in 1956 without an attribution more specific than "Anonymous Italian, sixteenth century," and it has only recently been recognized as a characteristic example of the mature Taddeo's draughtsmanship at its freest. A pen and wash drawing attributed to Taddeo, representing "The Bath of Diana," was once in Sir Thomas Lawrence's collection (*The Lawrence Gallery. Seventh Exhibition*, no. 23). This is no doubt the same as the "leaf of poetical designs, Venus bathing, on both sides, free pen and wash" in the collection of William Young Ottley (Ottley sale, London, 1814, no. 1491). The majority of the Zuccaro drawings that belonged to Lawrence are now in the Rosenbach Foundation in Philadelphia, and Janos Scholz possesses six further sheets from this source (see No. 136 of this exhibition), but there is no study of bathing nymphs in either group. The present sheet does not bear Lawrence's mark, but may even so be the drawing that belonged to him. The rather pneumatic reclining nymph at the right of the composition who stares out at the spectator can be recognized, as well as her companion nymphs, in a drawing in the Perman Collection in Stockholm that bears an old and correct attribution to Taddeo Zuccaro. The final form of the composition is known from a carefully finished drawing in the Louvre (Inv. 9030), traditionally, and in all probability correctly, attributed to Taddeo's contemporary, Orazio Sammacchini, a Bolognese artist known to have been active in Rome in the 1560s. J. A. Gere had already suggested that the Louvre drawing might preserve a composition by Taddeo Zuccaro, and the recent identification of the Metropolitan drawing fully confirms this suggestion.

PROVENANCE: Walter Lowry.

The Metropolitan Museum of Art
Gift of Walter Lowry, 56.219.3

135 *The Martyrdom of St. Paul*

Pen and brown ink, brown wash, heightened with white, over traces of black chalk. 19½ × 14⅞₆ inches (49.5 × 36.8 cm.). Horizontal fold at center.

J. A. Gere has identified this large drawing as a study for the fresco in the center of the vault of the Frangipani Chapel in S. Marcello al Corso, Rome, which was decorated by Taddeo Zuccaro with scenes from the life of St. Paul. He received the commission about 1557, but the decoration was still not quite finished at his death in September 1566. The ceiling frescoes would have been executed first, for obvious practical reasons. The composition has been simplified in the fresco where the background crowd, so brilliantly indicated in the drawing, is reduced to a few figures. It is a curious departure from standard iconography that the instrument of the saint's martyrdom, in both drawing and fresco, is an ax and not the traditional sword.

PROVENANCE: Sir Peter Lely (Lugt 2092).

Robert Lehman

136 *Pope Julius III Confirming Ottavio Farnese's Title to the Duchy of Parma*

Pen and brown ink, brown wash, over traces of black chalk. 15 × 21¹⁵⁄₁₆ inches (38.1 × 55.8 cm.). Vertical crease at center.

Verso: Composition studies in pen and brown ink, brown wash, over red chalk for other frescoes in the Sala dei Fatti Farnesiani at Caprarola: Paul III giving the baton of papal commander to Pier Luigi Farnese, and representations of Farnese marriages.

A free study by Taddeo for one of the frescoes ornamenting the Sala dei Fatti Farnesiani at Caprarola in the huge palace constructed by Vignola for the Farneses. The Sala dei Fatti, one of the principal rooms of the palace, is entirely decorated with frescoes by the Zuccaro brothers glorifying the deeds of the Farneses who, as fairly recent arrivals on the Italian political scene, were anxious to establish their claim to respectability. Here Ottavio Farnese kneels before Julius III with a model of the city of Parma in his hand, inviting papal confirmation of his claim to lordship of Parma and Piacenza. The composition of the fresco as executed has been considerably simplified. A *modello* based on this drawing is in the Louvre (R.F. 73); an old copy is in the Morgan Library (repr. Fairfax Murray, I, pl. 23).

PROVENANCE: Jonathan Richardson Senior (Lugt 2169); Thomas Dimsdale (Lugt 2426); Sir Thomas Lawrence; Samuel Woodburn; Lawrence-Woodburn sale, London, Christie's, June 4–8, 1860, part of no. 1074; Sir Thomas Phillipps, Cheltenham; T. Fitzroy Phillipps Fenwick; A. S. W. Rosenbach, New York.

Janos Scholz

Alessandro Allori
Florence 1535–Florence 1607

137 *The Judgment of Paris*

Pen and brown ink, brown wash, heightened with white, over black chalk, on blue paper. 14⅜ × 18⅝ inches (36.6 × 47.4 cm.). Vertical crease at center.

Paris is seated at right with a giant golden apple in his hand, while Mercury at center presents Minerva, Juno, and Venus, who are about to remove their clothes in preparation for the judging. Above at the left are parked the attributes of the three goddesses: a pair of owls, a pair of peacocks, and a swan-drawn chariot. Alessandro Allori's own account books recorded payments from the Grand Duke of Tuscany in 1583 for tapestry cartoons representing the story of the Judgment of Paris; if these tapestries were woven they do not seem to have survived (see I. B. Supino, *I Ricordi di Alessandro Allori*, Florence, 1908, p. 19). The Gabinetto Disegni e Stampe of the Uffizi possesses a number of drawings by Alessandro related to tapestry cartoons, and they are very similar in style to this highly finished sheet.

PROVENANCE: Purchased by the Metropolitan Museum in London, 1963.

EXHIBITIONS: London, Peter Claas, "Drawings of Five Centuries," 1963, no. 1, pl. 1.

The Metropolitan Museum of Art
Rogers Fund, 63.96

Giovanni de' Vecchi

Borgo San Sepolcro 1536–Rome 1614

138   *St. John the Evangelist*

Pen and brown ink, heightened with white, on light brown paper; squared for transfer in black chalk. Irregular circle, 10⅜ × 9¹⁵⁄₁₆ inches (26.4 × 25.2 cm.). Lined.

An eighteenth-century English inscription on the back of the old mount correctly identifies this drawing as a study for one of Giovanni de' Vecchi's most important commissions, the cartoons for two of the mosaic pendentives under Michelangelo's dome in St. Peter's. Cartoons for the figures of John the Evangelist and Luke were supplied by de' Vecchi; those for the figures of Matthew and Mark were designed by Cesare Nebbia (Giovanni Baglione, *Le Vite de' pittori scultori et architetti*, Rome, 1642, pp. 117, 128). Drawings by Giovanni de' Vecchi, an important and decidedly individual late Roman mannerist, are rare, and this document reveals him as a draughtsman with a loose and painterly style, somewhat unexpected from an artist of Tuscan origins.

PROVENANCE: Thomas Hudson (Lugt 2432); Sir Joshua Reynolds (Lugt 2364); Samuel Rogers, London; Rogers sale, London, Christie's, April 28, 1856 and eighteen days following, no. 941; sale, London, Sotheby's, December 1, 1964, no. 212, repr., bought by the Metropolitan Museum.

The Metropolitan Museum of Art
Purchase, Joseph Pulitzer Bequest, 64.295.3

Battista Naldini

Florence 1537–Florence 1591

139   *The Dead Christ Supported by Three Figures*

Pen and brown ink, brown wash, heightened with white, over black chalk, on brown washed paper. 12¼ × 9⅛ inches (31.1 × 23.2 cm.).

Formerly attributed to Palma Giovane, this drawing was identified by Philip Pouncey in 1958 as a typical example of Naldini's very personal and mannered draughtsmanship. A similar vertical composition with the dead Christ supported by three winged angels is studied in a drawing in the Rudolf Collection in London (Courtauld photograph 154/38 [2A]).

BIBLIOGRAPHY: Virch, *Baker Collection*, no. 16, repr.

Walter C. Baker

Federico Zuccaro

Sant' Angelo in Vado 1540/1541–Ancona 1609

140   *The Vision of St. Eustace*

Point of brush, brown, gray, green, yellow, and red wash, heightened with white over traces of black chalk; lightly squared in black chalk. 13⁷⁄₁₆ × 7¹⁵⁄₁₆ inches (34.1 × 20.2 cm.). Lined.

Finished squared study for a fresco executed on the façade of a small palace on the Piazza Sant' Eustachio in Rome about 1558–1559, when Federico Zuccaro was eighteen. Vasari recounts that this was Federico's first important commission, obtained for him by his already successful elder brother Taddeo, who interfered with the work in progress. Federico, enraged, destroyed his brother's additions. Through the intervention of friends peace was made between the brothers, and once Federico had finished the fresco it was hailed as a triumph for the young artist. The relevant passage from Vasari was transcribed on the back of the old mount by the Richardsons, who once owned the drawing. The fresco decoration survives in a damaged and repainted state. It differed from monochrome Roman wall frescoes of the earlier sixteenth century in that it was executed in a variety of colors, already present in this drawing.

PROVENANCE: Jonathan Richardson Senior (Lugt 2184); Jonathan Richardson Junior (Lugt 2170); Sir Joshua Reynolds (Lugt 2364); purchased by the Metropolitan Museum in London, 1962.

BIBLIOGRAPHY: J. Bean, *Metropolitan Museum of Art Bulletin*, March 1963, p. 232, fig. 5; J. A. Gere, "Two Panel-pictures by Taddeo Zuccaro—II," *Burlington Magazine*, CV, 1963, p. 394, n. 12; Bean, *100 European Drawings*, no. 26, repr.

The Metropolitan Museum of Art
Rogers Fund, 62.76

141 *Porta Virtutis: Minerva Triumphant over Ignorance and Calumny*

Pen and brown ink, brown wash, over a little black chalk. 15¼ × 11¹⁄₁₆ inches (38.7 × 28.1 cm.).

Hermann Voss was the first to point out, apropos of a version of this drawing at Frankfort-on-the-Main, that the composition must be that of the painting of Calumny which Federico Zuccaro exhibited in 1580 on the feast day of St. Luke, the patron of painters, on the façade of the church then dedicated to the saint in Rome. According to Baglione, Federico painted this picture as a gesture of revenge against certain members of the papal household who had criticized his paintings in the Cappella Paolina. He depicted his critics with asses' ears, which so enraged the Pope that Federico was obliged to flee Rome. Another version of the drawing is at Christ Church, Oxford (repr. *Rivista d'Arte*, XXXIII, 1958, p. 49; the Frankfort version repr. *ibid.*, XXXII, 1957, p. 192, and Voss, *Malerei der Spätrenaissance in Rom und Florenz*, Berlin, 1920, fig. 245). All three are undoubtedly by Federico's own hand, but it is not certain whether they are preliminary studies for the picture or records of it made by the artist himself. Federico's composition is dominated by the armed figure of Minerva, who stands guard at the *Porta Virtutis*. The allegorical figures are identified by inscriptions in Federico's hand. Chief among these are Crass Ignorance, seated in the left foreground listening to Adulation and Persuasion who whisper into his ass's ears, Envy writhing on the ground in the center, and on the right a satyr, the minister of Envy, who points toward the impregnable portal.

BIBLIOGRAPHY: Detlef Heikamp, "Vicende di Federigo Zuccari," *Rivista d'Arte*, XXXII, 1957, pp. 189–194; Detlef Heikamp, "Ancora su Federico Zuccari," *Rivista d'Arte*, XXXIII, 1958, pp. 45–50.

EXHIBITIONS: Indianapolis, Pontormo to Greco, 1954, no. 39, repr.; Hamburg, Scholz Exhibition, 1963, no. 178, pl. 57; New Haven, Scholz Exhibition, 1964, no. 54.

Janos Scholz

Cherubino Alberti

Borgo San Sepolcro 1542–Rome 1615

142 *Design for a Medallion with Papal Arms*

Pen and brown ink, brown wash, over black chalk. Diameter 8½ inches (21.5 cm.).

Allegorical figures of Justice and Fortitude here flank a globe bearing the arms of Pope Clement VIII Aldobrandini; above, a putto wearing a papal crown brandishes a pontifical key and a banderole inscribed *VIII P. M.* (Pontifex Maximus). In 1596 Pope Clement commissioned Cherubino Alberti and his slightly younger brother Giovanni to decorate the Sala Clementina in the Vatican. Work on this elaborate project, a pre-baroque fantasy of illusionistic architecture peopled with figures, kept both brothers and their assistants busy for several years, and the exact share of each artist is unclear. It has recently been convincingly argued that the younger Giovanni was the more inventive of the two (see Maria Vittoria Brugnoli in *Bollettino d'Arte*, 1960, pp. 223 ff.). This drawing was attributed to Cherubino by Voss, and indeed the group seen in steep perspective in a circular opening is close to decorative groups on the walls of the Sala Clementina. The wall decoration, as opposed to the ceiling fresco, is specifically attributed to Cherubino in certain sources.

PROVENANCE: Hermann Voss, Berlin.

BIBLIOGRAPHY: Hermann Voss, *Zeichnungen der italienischen Spätrenaissance*, Munich, 1928, pl. 26.

EXHIBITIONS: Hamburg, Scholz Exhibition, 1963, no. 2, pl. 47; New Haven, Scholz Exhibition, 1964, no. 22.

Janos Scholz

Niccolò Martinelli, called Trometta

Pesaro early 1540s–Rome (?) before 1621

143 *St. Matthew*

Pen and brown ink, brown wash, heightened with white; two small sketches at lower right in pen and gray-black ink; squared in red chalk, on faded blue paper. 16 × 10⅝ inches (40.6 × 23.3 cm.). Somewhat abraded, old fold at center, crease at right, losses at corners, especially at upper right, some breaks. Lined.

A preparatory study for the figure of one of the four Evangelists in the fresco decoration of the choir of the Roman church of S. Maria in Aracoeli, the masterwork (1566–1568) of the artist. Trometta's style as a draughtsman dependent on Taddeo Zuccaro has only recently been brought into focus by J. A. Gere, although early investigation was done by Hermann Voss (*Zeichnungen der italienischen Spätrenaissance*, Munich, 1928, no. 23), who first identified the oval composition *Virgin and Child in Glory* in Munich with the Aracoeli fresco. In all, eight drawings connected with the Aracoeli commission are known.

PROVENANCE: Hugh N. Squire; purchased by the Pierpont Morgan Library in London, 1962.

BIBLIOGRAPHY: J. A. Gere, "Drawings by Niccolò Martinelli, Il Trometta," *Master Drawings*, I, no. 4, 1963, pp. 10, 17, pl. 4; J. A. Gere, "Two Panel Pictures by Taddeo Zuccaro and some Related Compositions—II: the 'Agony in the Garden' in the Strossmayer Gallery, Zagreb," *Burlington Magazine*, CV, 1963, no. 726, p. 395, n. 10; Morgan Library, *Thirteenth Fellows Report, 1963–1964*, p. 91.

The Pierpont Morgan Library
Gift of the Fellows, 1962.17

Jacopo Bertoia

Parma 1544–Parma 1574

144 *Music-Making Figures and Lovers*

Pen and brown ink, brown wash, heightened with white, over traces of black chalk, on light brown paper; squared in black chalk. 5³⁄₁₆ × 9⅝ inches (13.2 × 24.5 cm.).

Popham, who knew this sheet through the reversed eighteenth-century facsimile reproduction published as Parmigianino, was the first to recognize that the drawing is a study by Bertoia for a group of music-making figures that appears on one of the walls of the Sala del Bacio in the Palazzo del Giardino at Parma (the relevant detail of the fresco is reproduced by Ghidiglia Quintavalle, pls. XXXIV, XXXVI). The frescoes in the Sala del Bacio (the Room of the Kiss) form a particularly felicitous

and fantastic late mannerist complex; the music-makers of the present drawing are seen on one of the walls of the room, surrounded by embracing couples, in a hall supported by transparent crystal columns. These frescoes, a project in which the mysterious Girolamo Mirola collaborated with Bertoia, are datable about 1570–1573. Other drawings for the Sala del Bacio are in the Uffizi and the École des Beaux-Arts in Paris.

PROVENANCE: Caleb Whitefoord (when engraved by Metz); Louis Rorimer, Cleveland.

BIBLIOGRAPHY: Metz, *Imitations of Drawings*, repr. p. 74 (engraved in reverse, attributed to Parmigianino); Rudolph Weigel, *Die Werke der Maler in ihren Handzeichnungen*, Leipzig, 1865, p. 489, no. 5836 (as Parmigianino); Popham, *Parmigianino*, p. 18; Augusta Ghidiglia Quintavalle, *Il Bertoja*, Milan, 1963, pp. 35, 54–55 (the Metz facsimile mentioned but not connected with the present drawing), pl. XXXVIIa (wrongly described as being in the École des Beaux-Arts, Paris).

EXHIBITIONS: New York, Wildenstein, "Masters of Seven Centuries, Paintings and Drawings from the Fourteenth to Twentieth Century, for the Benefit of Wellesley College," 1962, no. 9, repr. p. 27.

James J. Rorimer

Jacopo Palma, called Palma Giovane

Venice 1544–Venice 1628

145 *Virgin and Child in the Clouds Adored by Five Saints*

Pen and brown ink, brown wash, over red chalk indications. 15⅜ × 8⁵⁄₁₆ inches (38.9 × 21.1 cm.). No watermark.

Verso: Several studies in pen and brown ink, and one in red chalk, of St. Jerome, and another figure in pen and brown ink.

A general compositional study for the altarpiece in the first chapel on the right in the church of S. Zaccaria at Venice (Venturi, IX, Part 7, p. 227, repr.), executed in the opening years of the seventeenth century, but looking back to the High Renaissance. On the verso are further sketches for the St. Jerome and another figure. The figure of St. Sebastian was also separately studied in two different sheets of the second Munich album of Palma's drawings (II, 12 and 35). The fact, as the Tietzes remarked, that Munich II, 12 occurs on the back of a letter dated 1605 supplies a *terminus post quem* for the date of the execution of the drawings and altarpiece.

PROVENANCE: Charles Fairfax Murray; purchased by J. Pierpont Morgan in London, 1910.

BIBLIOGRAPHY: Tietze, *Venetian Drawings*, no. 1051, pl. CLXXX, 4; Florence, Uffizi, *Mostra di disegni di Jacopo Palma il Giovane*, 1958, p. 15, under no. 6.

EXHIBITIONS: New London, Fourth Anniversary Exhibition, 1936, no. 37; Toledo, Venetian Painting, 1940, no. 83; Northampton, Smith College, Italian Drawings, 1941, no. 38; Toronto, Art Gallery of Toronto, "Titian, Tintoretto, Paolo Veronese," 1960, no. 38.

The Pierpont Morgan Library
No. IV, 84A

Giacomo Ligozzi

Verona about 1547–Florence 1626

146 *The Allegory of Death*

Pen and brown ink, brown wash, heightened with white on paper tinted brown. 14¹¹⁄₁₆ × 11⅛ inches (37.3 × 28.3 cm.). Water stain at lower left corner, crease at lower right corner. Lined.

Signed at lower left in pen and brown ink with monogram and dated *1597*. Inscribed in a cartouche at the top, *La morte e fin d'una prigion' oscura*; at right, *si mosse; e disse: o tu donna che vai | Dopo l'imprese perigliose et vane*; at left, *nel mezo del camin di nostra vitta*; at lower center, *e di Tua vita il termine non sai*. Various inscriptions regarding collections on the verso and on the mount.

As was recognized by Dr. John Percy in 1876 when this drawing was in his possession, the artist took the three principal figures of the composition from the chiaroscuro woodcut *The Lovers Surprised by Death* (*Der Tod und das Liebespaar*), 1510, by Hans Burgkmair the Elder. The artist's literary learning is displayed in the inscribed lines from Dante, including the famous "nel mezzo del cammin di nostra vita," the opening words of the *Inferno*, placed below the figures of the small boy and girl already reined with Death.

PROVENANCE: John Talman (according to inscription on verso); N. F. Haym (Lugt 1970); The Earls Spencer (Lugt 1530); Spencer sale, London, T. Philipe, June 13, 1811, no. 408 (as Lambert Hopfer); Thomas Dimsdale (Lugt 2426); Dr. John Percy (Lugt 1504); Charles Fairfax Murray; purchased by J. Pierpont Morgan in London, 1910.

BIBLIOGRAPHY: Fairfax Murray, I, no. 51, repr.; J. Byam

Shaw, "The Prototype of a Subject by Giacomo Ligozzi," *Art Quarterly*, XIX, 1956, pp. 283–284, fig. 1.

The Pierpont Morgan Library
No. I, 91

Bernardino Barbatelli, called Poccetti

Florence 1548–Florence 1612

147 *The Blessed Filippo Benizzi Admonishing Two Wicked Women*

Brush and gray wash, heightened with white, on brownish paper. 9¹⁵⁄₁₆ × 13⅝ inches (25.3 × 34.6 cm.). Upper left corner missing; crease at upper right margin.

Study for a lunette-shaped fresco painted by Poccetti on the southeast wall of the large cloister flanking the SS. Annunziata in Florence. The drawing differs in many details from the fresco; in the latter the two wicked women are seen from behind kneeling in a pose derived from Raphael's *Expulsion of Heliodorus*. Other preparatory drawings for this fresco are in the Albertina (repr. *Beschreibender Katalog*, III, *Die Zeichnungen der toskanischen, umbrischen und römischen Schulen*, Vienna, 1932, no. 303) and the Musée Fabre in Montpellier. This last drawing, formerly attributed to the French school, was very recently identified by Roseline Bacou. Poccetti's frescoes in the Annunziata date from about 1605, and they reveal, as does this drawing, the dominance of Andrea del Sarto in Florentine art. Here Poccetti's graceful grouping of figures in a landscape must be inspired by Andrea's frescoes in the small cloister of the SS. Annunziata, painted nearly one hundred years earlier.

PROVENANCE: Professor J. Isaacs, London; Isaacs sale, London, Sotheby's, February 27, 1964, no. 16, bought by the Metropolitan Museum.

The Metropolitan Museum of Art
Rogers Fund, 64.48.1

Ambrogio Figino

Milan 1548–Milan 1608

148 *Album of Drawings*

Twenty-one drawings pasted on nineteen of a total of twenty-one folios; seven in red chalk, nine in black chalk, four in red and black chalk, and one in red and black chalk with outlines in pen and brown ink. Comments by Padre Sebastiano Resta (1635–1714) at the bottom of each folio;

a letter from Padre Resta to Francesco Gabburri is tipped into the front. Bound in red morocco, tooled in gold. Binding: 8¾ × 5¾ inches (22.2 × 14.6 cm.).

This interesting album was put together and annotated by Padre Sebastiano Resta, member of the congregation of St. Philip Neri at Rome and an omnivorous collector of drawings. Tipped into the album is a letter dated Rome, October 4, 1710, addressed by the Padre to the Florentine collector Francesco Maria Gabburri, who once owned the landscape drawings by Fra Bartolomeo in the exhibition (Nos. 30–34). The letter indicates that the album originally contained twenty-four drawings by Figino (today there are only twenty-one), and Resta comments on the rarity of the artist's drawings, even in his native Milan, because of the loss at sea of part of his *oeuvre*.

Many of the drawings are copies after Leonardo, Raphael, and Michelangelo, but some, like that exhibited, are of Figino's own invention as well as execution. The red chalk drawing of a horseman in a long cloak, folio 6, apparently records a lost drawing by Leonardo. (For other copies of lost drawings by Leonardo in the exhibition, see No. 150.)

The paintings of Figino, who was extolled in verse by Torquato Tasso, are still plentiful in the churches of Milan, and an album of 120 of his drawings is preserved at Windsor Castle.

PROVENANCE: Padre Sebastiano Resta (Lugt 2992); Francesco Maria Gabburri; William Kent (?); Earl of Yarborough, Brocklesby Park; purchased by the Pierpont Morgan Library in London, 1964.

BIBLIOGRAPHY: A. E. Popham, "On a Book of Drawings by Ambrogio Figino," *Bibliothèque d'Humanisme et Renaissance, Travaux et Documents*, XX, 1958, pp. 266–276, figs. 1–4; Morgan Library, *Thirteenth Fellows Report, 1963–1964*, pp. 92–94, repr.

The Pierpont Morgan Library
Gift of Mr. and Mrs. Carl Stern, 1964.1

Lavinia Fontana

Bologna 1552–Rome 1614

149 *Album of Drawings*

Nineteen portrait drawings pasted on nineteen of a total of twenty folios. Black and red chalk. Bound in black mo-rocco, tooled in gold. Binding: 14¾ × 11¼ inches (33.4 × 28.4 cm.).

The drawing on folio 2 is inscribed in pen and brown ink, *Ritrato di Lavinia | propria.*

The second of the nineteen portraits gathered together in a late seventeenth-century album is that of the artist herself. Most of the likenesses are those of men and women of fashion or priests and nuns, but folio 8 shows a startling red-bearded lady.

The daughter and pupil of Prospero Fontana, Lavinia enjoyed considerable popularity in Rome as a portraitist, working first under Pope Gregory XIII, who like the Fontana family was a native of Bologna, and later under Clement VIII.

PROVENANCE: Lord Palmerston (according to Fairfax Murray); Charles Fairfax Murray; purchased by J. Pierpont Morgan in London, 1910.

BIBLIOGRAPHY: Fairfax Murray, IV, no. 158, folio 2, repr.

The Pierpont Morgan Library
No. IV, 158

Anonymous Milanese Artist

About 1560–1580

150 *Codex Huygens*

Three leaves from a total of 128 comprising textual and illustrative material for a projected treatise, *Le Regole del disegno*. Ordinarily the drawings are kept loose between the leaves of a seventeenth-century gold-tooled red morocco album ordered for this purpose by Constantine Huygens.

Folio 28. *Illustration of the Lateral Bending and Turning to Profile of the Chest in Combination with the Turning of the Head and Folding of the Limbs*. Pen and brown and red inks, and leadpoint. 7⅜ × 5⁵⁄₁₆ inches (18.7 × 13.3 cm.). Watermark: serpent, fragment.

Folio 75. *Dimensioned Drawings of Horses' Heads*. Drawing in upper half is after drawing in Leonardo's Ms. H. at the Institut de France; lower half is a free copy after a drawing at the Royal Library at Windsor Castle (Clark 12286). Pen and brown ink, and leadpoint. 7⅛ × 5¼ inches (18.1 × 13.5 cm.).

Folio 90. *Demonstration of Effect of Shadows Cast by Artificial Light*. (Shadows appear proportionately enlarged as object approaches the candle and moves away from wall.) Pen and brown ink, and black and red chalk. 7⅛ × 9⅛ inches (18.2 × 23.1 cm.). Watermark: crowned serpent with the initials B. M. (Briquet 13691).

The Codex Huygens takes its name from its seventeenth-century Dutch owner, the accomplished Constantine Huygens, who for more than sixty years served the House of Orange, including William III of England. Huygens believed that the codex was the work of Leonardo and remarked that he would not part with it for four times the three and a half guineas it cost him. It was he who put the codex in its present form, a dealer in prints called Cooper being responsible for the mending and mounting of the leaves, and the bookbinder Harding for the morocco album.

The 128 surviving pages of the projected *Regole del disegno* deal with the structure and proportions of the male and female figure; a theory of human movement; the proportions of the horse; perspective; and a theory of light and shade.

The Milanese artist-author apparently had access to the writings and drawings of Leonardo da Vinci before they were dispersed, as a number of drawings are copied or traced from Leonardo's studies in human and equine proportions, and others seem to preserve the subjects of lost originals. A. E. Popham maintains that notwithstanding Erwin Panofsky's arguments against the authorship of Bernardino Campi (1522–after 1584), the style of the drawings does point to his hand. Anyone comparing the figures of the codex with Bernardino's cannot fail to be impressed by certain stylistic similarities.

PROVENANCE: Remy (Remigius) von Leemput (died before April 30, 1677); Constantine Huygens (purchased in London from "Mrs. Remy," March 2, 1690, for 3½ guineas); purchased by the Pierpont Morgan Library in London, 1938.

BIBLIOGRAPHY: *Journal van Constantijn Huygens, den Zoon, van 21 Oct. 1688 tot 2 Sept. 1696 (Werken, uitgegeven door het Historisch Genootschap te Utrecht, Nieuwe Reeks*, XXIII), 1876, pp. 240 ff.; *Oeuvres complètes de Christiaan Huygens, publiées par la Société Hollandaise des Sciences*, IX, Amsterdam, 1901, p. 379, no. 2569; M. W. M. Mensing, "De Leonardo's van Constantijn Huygens den Zoon," *Feestbundel, Dr. Abraham Bredius aangebooden . . .*, Amsterdam, 1915, pp. 186 ff., pls. 80–81; Kenneth Clark, *Drawings of Leonardo da Vinci at Windsor Castle*, Cambridge, 1935, pp. xii–xiii; Otto Kurz, "A Contribution to the History of Leonardo Drawings," *Burlington Magazine*, LXIX, 1936, pp. 135 ff.; Erwin Panofsky, *The Codex Huygens and Leonardo da Vinci's Art Theory: The Pierpont Morgan Library Codex M.A. 1139* (Studies of the Warburg Institute, XIII),

London, 1940; Kate Trauman Steinitz, *Leonardo da Vinci's trattato della pittura*, Copenhagen, 1958, pp. 134–137; A. E. Popham, "On a Book of Drawings by Ambrogio Figino," *Bibliothèque d'Humanisme et Renaissance, Travaux et Documents*, XX, 1958, p. 274, n. 3; Carlo Pedretti, "Leonardo on Curvilinear Perspective," *Bibliothèque d'Humanisme et Renaissance, Travaux et Documents*, XXV, 1963, pp. 79–80, repr.; Carlo Pedretti, *Leonardo da Vinci, On Painting, a Lost Book (Libro A)*, Berkeley and Los Angeles, 1964, *passim*; Carlo Pedretti, "Excerpts from the Codex Huygens Published in London in 1720," *Journal of the Warburg Institute*, XXVIII, 1965, pp. 336–338.

The Pierpont Morgan Library
M.A. 1139

Francesco Vanni

Siena 1563–Siena 1610

151 *The Virgin with St. Catherine and St. Bernardino of Siena*

Pen and brown ink, brown wash, over black chalk, on brownish paper. 8³⁄₁₆ × 10¾ inches (20.8 × 27.3 cm.). Lined.

Inscribed in pen and brown ink at lower right, *Vanni*; at lower left, *2*.

Vanni offers a synthesis of Sienese imagery in this spirited composition sketch. The Virgin, patroness of the city and the preferred subject of Sienese painting from the thirteenth through the sixteenth centuries, appears surrounded by angels and putti and adored by St. Bernardino and St. Catherine, protectors of the city. Below is indicated the skyline of Siena, easily identified by the silhouettes of the Torre del Mangia and of the cupola and campanile of the Duomo. The limits of the composition, which cannot be related to a surviving picture, are indicated by lines above and to the right; further to the right the artist has sketched ornamental motifs supporting heraldic animals.

PROVENANCE: Padre Sebastiano Resta, Milan; Monsignor Giovanni Matteo Marchetti, bishop of Arezzo; Cavaliere Marchetti of Pistoia; John, Lord Somers (Lugt 2981); Richard Houlditch (Lugt 2214); Jonathan Richardson Senior (Lugt 2183, 2995, 2996, 2983, 2984, 2992); Sir Joshua Reynolds (Lugt 2364); Hugh N. Squire, London; purchased by the Metropolitan Museum in London, 1962.

BIBLIOGRAPHY: Bean, *100 European Drawings*, no. 29, repr.

The Metropolitan Museum of Art
Gustavus A. Pfeiffer Fund, 62.120.8

Plates

I · FRA FILIPPO LIPPI (?) · St. Matthew
Private Collection

2 · PESELLINO · St. Philip

The Metropolitan Museum of Art

3 · GIOVANNI BELLINI · Christ's Descent into Limbo   Robert Lehman

4 · GIOVANNI BELLINI · St. Jerome in a Landscape   Robert Lehman

5 · GIOVANNI BELLINI, studio of · Last Supper

6 · ANTONIO POLLAIUOLO · Study for an Equestrian Monument   Robert Lehman

7 · ANTONIO POLLAIUOLO · Seated Saint   Robert Lehman

8 · COSSA · Venus Embracing Cupid at the Forge of Vulcan

9 · FRANCESCO DI SIMONE, attributed to · Page from a Sketchbook   Walter C. Baker

II · BOTTICELLI · Fragment of an Adoration of the Magi
The Pierpont Morgan Library

12 · FRANCESCO FRANCIA · Judith and Holofernes   The Pierpont Morgan Library

13 · BERNARDINO DEI CONTI · Head of a Man   Benjamin Sonnenberg

14 · BARTOLOMEO MONTAGNA · Nude Man beside a Pedestal
Private Collection

15 · LEONARDO · Studies for a Nativity
The Metropolitan Museum of Art

16 · LEONARDO · Head of a Man
The Metropolitan Museum of Art

17 · LEONARDO · Allegory
The Metropolitan Museum of Art

18 · LEONARDO · Study of a Bear
Robert Lehman

20 · ERCOLE DE' ROBERTI · Flagellation   Robert Lehman

21 · FILIPPINO LIPPI · Christ and the Magdalene

The Pierpont Morgan Library

21 (verso) · FILIPPINO LIPPI · Youth with Sword and Kneeling Youth with Staff
The Pierpont Morgan Library

23 · *VITTORE CARPACCIO* · Youth in Armor
The Metropolitan Museum of Art

24 · PIERO DI COSIMO, attributed to · Head of a Young Woman
Walter C. Baker

25 · RAFFAELLINO DEL GARBO · Angel of the Annunciation
The Metropolitan Museum of Art

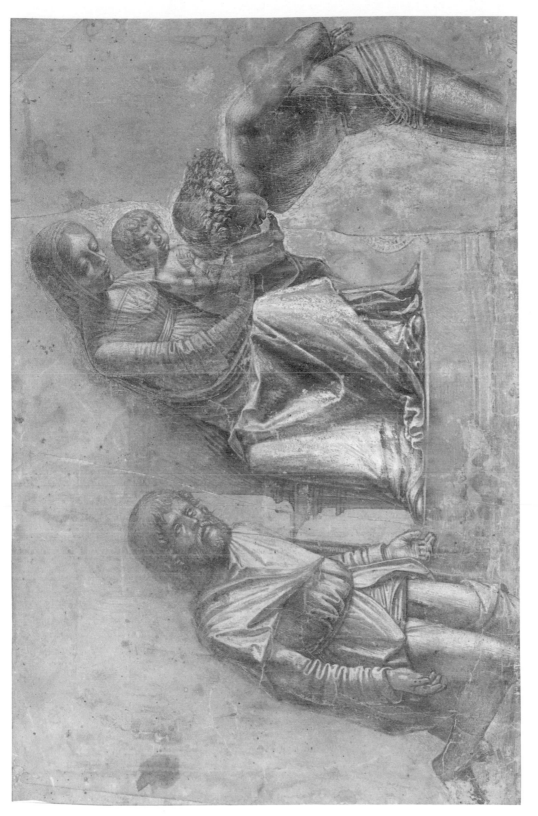

26 · FRANCESCO MORONE · Virgin and Child with St. Roch and St. Sebastian

27 · FRA BARTOLOMEO · Adoration of the Magi
Walter C. Baker

28 · FRA BARTOLOMEO · Virgin with the Holy Children
Robert Lehman

29 · FRA BARTOLOMEO · Virgin and Child with Saints and Angels   The Pierpont Morgan Library

30 · FRA BARTOLOMEO · Approach to a Mountain Village   Robert Lehman

31 · FRA BARTOLOMEO · Town on the Crest of a Slope   The Metropolitan Museum of Art

32 · FRA BARTOLOMEO · Fiesole from the Mugnone Valley,

33 · FRA BARTOLOMEO · Monastery Church and Well

Walter C. Baker

35 · AMICO ASPERTINI · Bacchanalian Scene

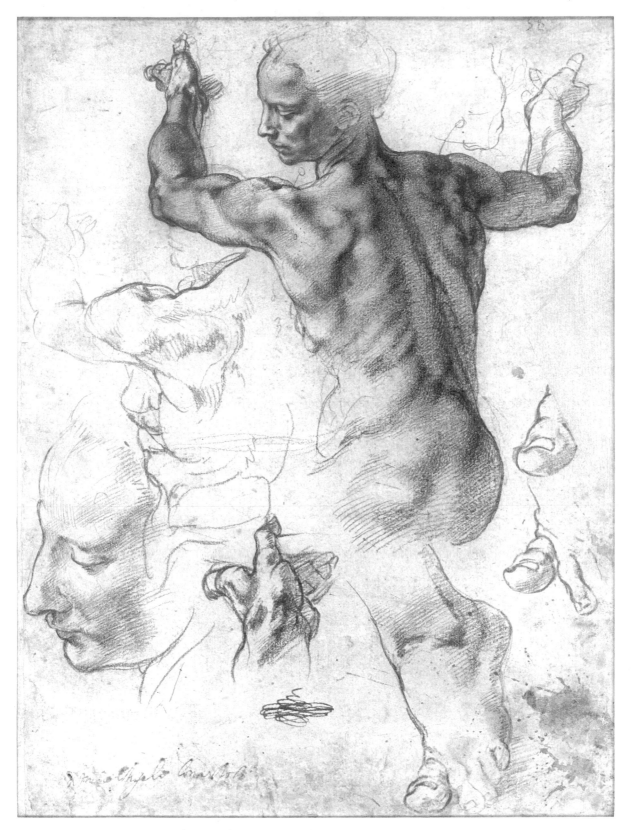

36 · MICHELANGELO · Studies for the Libyan Sibyl   The Metropolitan Museum of Art

36 (verso) · MICHELANGELO · Studies of Legs, a Knee, and of a Figure
The Metropolitan Museum of Art

a

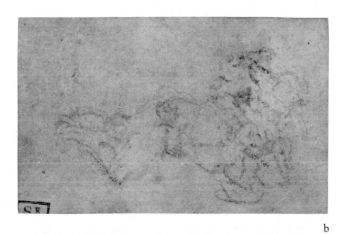

b

c

d

37 · MICHELANGELO
David Slaying Goliath
The Pierpont Morgan Library

38 · NICCOLÒ GIOLFINO · Betrayal of Christ

39 · CESARE DA SESTO · Adam and Eve; Two Male Figures
The Pierpont Morgan Library

39 A · CESARE DA SESTO · Judgment of Solomon; Virgin and Child
The Pierpont Morgan Library

40 · GIORGIONE · Landscape with Old Man

41 · VINCENZO CATENA · Study of Drapery   Janos Scholz

42 · GAUDENZIO FERRARI · Angel Playing a Violoncello   Private Collection

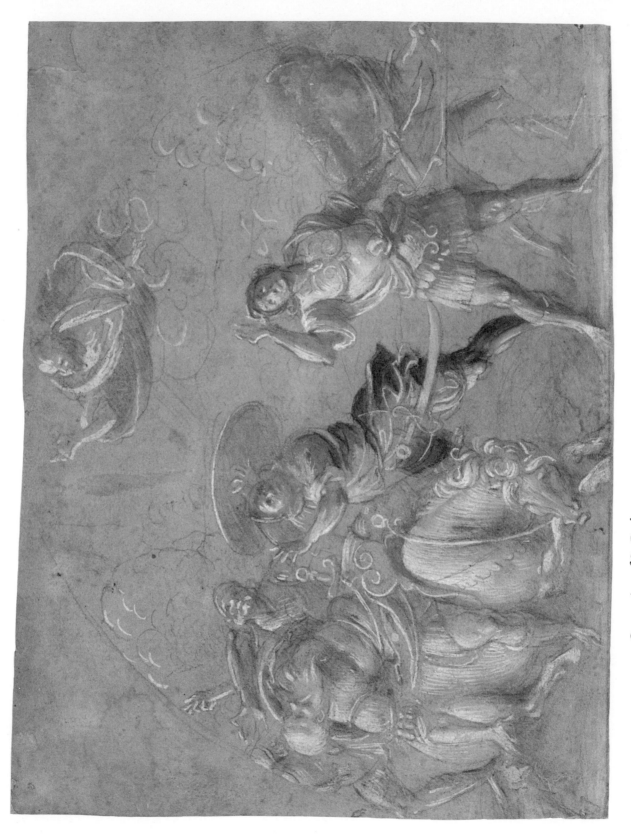

43 · GAUDENZIO FERRARI · Conversion of St. Paul

44 · LOTTO · Figure Reaching Upward   Janos Scholz

45 · LOTTO · St. Martin Dividing His Cloak   S. Schwarz Collection

46 · BERNARDINO LUINI · St. Lawrence before the Prefect of Rome

47 · BALDASSARE PERUZZI · Holy Family with Saints and Donor
The Pierpont Morgan Library

48 · RAPHAEL · Agony in the Garden

49 · RAPHAEL · Madonna and Child with St. John   The Metropolitan Museum of Art

49 (verso) · RAPHAEL · Nude Male Figure   The Metropolitan Museum of Art

50 · RAPHAEL · Figure Symbolizing an Earthquake
Janos Scholz

51 · PORDENONE · Crucifixion
The Pierpont Morgan Library

52 · PORDENONE · St. Christopher   The Metropolitan Museum of Art

53 · PORDENONE · Conversion of St. Paul

54 · ROMANINO · Concert Champêtre

Hieromino Romanino da Bressa

55 · ROMANINO · Soldier with a Plumed Hat, Sketch of Another   Janos Scholz

Nude Male Figure
The Metropolitan
Museum of Art

57 · SEBASTIANO DEL PIOMBO · Sibyl
The Metropolitan Museum of Art

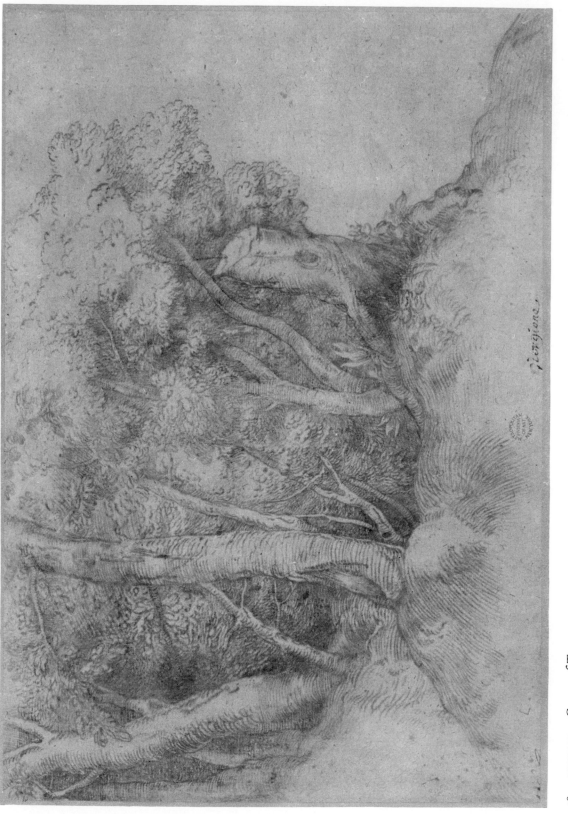

58 · TITIAN · Group of Trees

59 · TITIAN, attributed to · Two Satyrs in a Landscape   Curtis O. Baer

61 · BECCAFUMI · Head of Thrasybulus
The Pierpont Morgan Library

62 · BECCAFUMI · Head of the Good Thief

The Pierpont Morgan Library

64 · BECCAFUMI · Gaius Mucius Scaevola

65 · CORREGGIO · Head of a Woman　　　　　The Pierpont Morgan Library

66 · CORREGGIO · Adoration of the Magi   The Metropolitan Museum of Art

67 · CORREGGIO · Male Figure and Putto
Janos Scholz

68 · CORREGGIO · Annunciation
The Metropolitan Museum of Art

69 · CORREGGIO · Design for a Pilaster   The Metropolitan Museum of Art

70 · CORREGGIO · Allegory of Virtue   Robert and Bertina Suida Manning

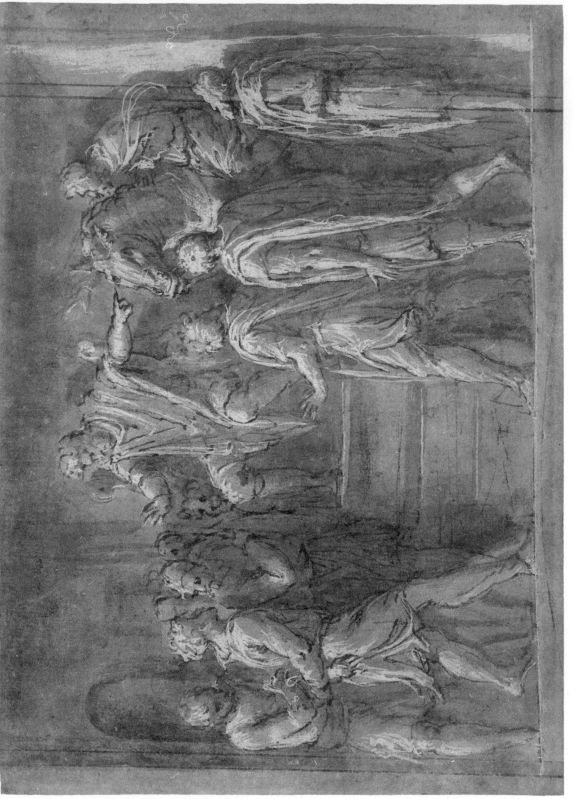

71 · POLIDORO DA CARAVAGGIO · Scene of Judgment

Robert and Bertina Suida Manning

73 · POLIDORO DA CARAVAGGIO · Studies for the Virgin Enthroned with Saints

David Playing the Harp
The Metropolitan Museum of Art

75 · BACCIO BANDINELLI · Three Male Heads
The Metropolitan Museum of Art

76 · PONTORMO · Standing Nude and Two Seated Nudes
The Pierpont Morgan Library

76 (verso) · PONTORMO · Striding Nude   The Pierpont Morgan Library

Roſso Fiorentino

Giulia Gonzaga Duchei
di Mantoa

77 · ROSSO FIORENTINO · Head of a Woman   The Metropolitan Museum of Art

78 · BATTISTA FRANCO
Standing Male Nude
The Metropolitan Museum of Art

79 · GIULIO ROMANO
Arms of the
Cardinal Gonzaga
The Pierpont
Morgan Library

82 · BENVENUTO CELLINI
Standing Male Nude with a Club

Ian Woodner

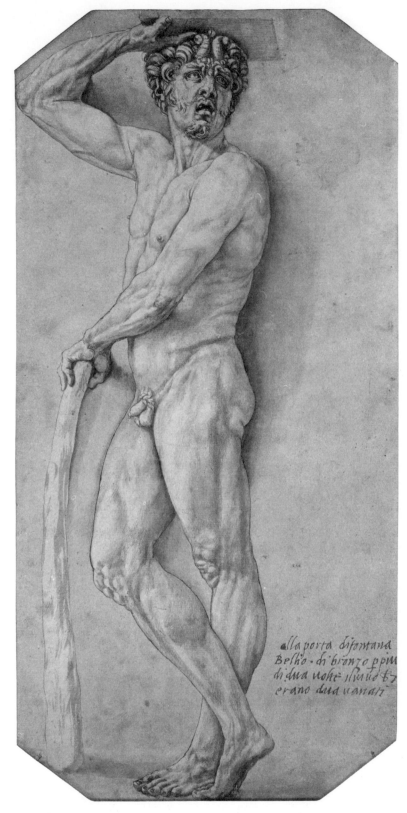

84 · PERINO DEL VAGA · Presentation of the Virgin
The Metropolitan Museum of Art

85 · PERINO DEL VAGA · Pool of Bethesda
The Pierpont Morgan Library

86 · PERINO DEL VAGA · Miracle of the Loaves and Fishes
The Pierpont Morgan Library

87 · PERINO DEL VAGA
Prudence
The Metropolitan
Museum of Art

88 · PARMIGIANINO · Three Putti
The Pierpont Morgan Library

89 · **PARMIGIANINO** · Putti and a Seated Boy
Janos Scholz

90 · PARMIGIANINO · Holy Family with Angels and Shepherds   Stephen Currier

91 · PARMIGIANINO · Adoration of the Shepherds   The Metropolitan Museum of Art

92 · PARMIGIANINO · Study for a Marriage of the Virgin

93 · PARMIGIANINO · Infant Christ on the Lap of the Virgin   The Pierpont Morgan Library

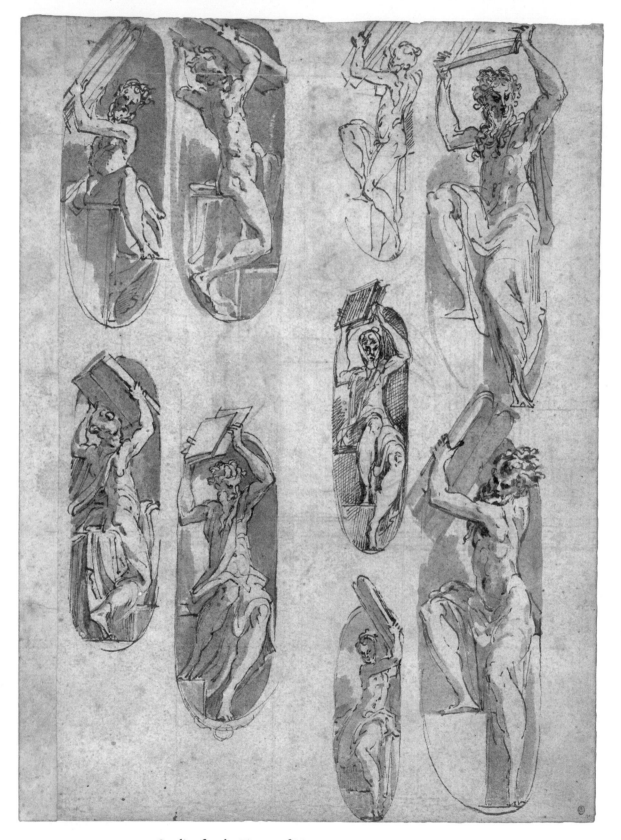

94 · PARMIGIANINO · Studies for the Figure of Moses
The Metropolitan Museum of Art

94 (verso) · PARMIGIANINO · Studies for the Figure of Eve and Architectural Studies
The Metropolitan Museum of Art

95 · PARMIGIANINO · Painter's Studio
The Pierpont Morgan Library

Giovanni Battista da Bologna.

97 · PRIMATICCIO · Vulcan Forging the Darts of Cupid
The Metropolitan Museum of Art

98 · PRIMATICCIO · Discord at the Marriage Feast of Peleus and Thetis
The Metropolitan Museum of Art

99 · POMPONIO AMALTEO · Flight into Egypt
The Pierpont Morgan Library

100 · LEONE LEONI, attributed to · Studies of the Head of Andrea Doria
The Pierpont Morgan Library

101 · FRANCESCO SALVIATI · Pope Presenting an Object to a Warrior

102 · FRANCESCO SALVIATI · Head of a Bearded Man

103 · FRANCESCO SALVIATI · Fantastic Emblem
Janos Scholz

104 · GIORGIO VASARI · Annunciation
The Pierpont Morgan Library

105 · LELIO ORSI · Flight into Egypt   The Pierpont Morgan Library

106 · LELIO ORSI · Design for a Façade

107 · NICCOLÒ
DELL' ABBATE
Peace
Private Collection

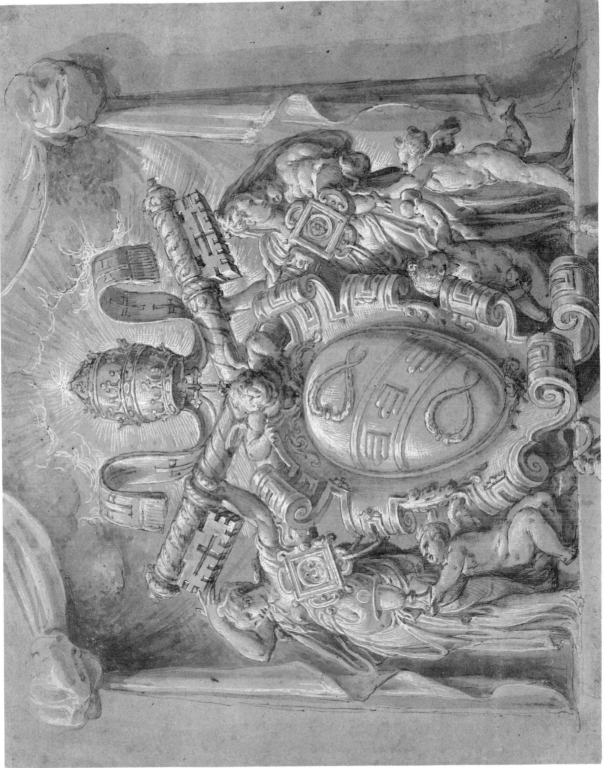

108 · NICCOLÒ DELL' ABBATE · Arms of Pope Julius III

Two Male Figures
The Metropolitan
Museum of Art

ERNESTVS ·VI·HENRICI   FRANCISCVS·III·HENRICI
XX· FILIVS   XX· FILIVS

fratres Luneburgenses duces

obijt 1456   obijt 1549·

E' cosa necessaria seguitare l'ordine di porre la nativita di Hippolyto, oue si uegga lucina cioe' Diana che
dale fasce l'amo, essendo propicia ale Donne partoreuti, ar'alla casta giouentu', la quale prese come in tucela
Hippolyto, et dafanciullo infino all'ultimo cenla Deita' l'accompagno et seco stese', Essa fu' quella che lo trasse
dal pericolo dela morte conlo aiuto di Aesculapio: essa le telse dala Calumnsia di Phedra amante terribile
et maligna; che presso Theseo lhauea posto indisgratia et dal stato di Troizene cacciata. essa fatto assapere
à Theseo come el caso era successo, come Hippolyto non hauea uoluto consentire al furore dela matregna;
era stato accusato perlo oppio; cosi Phedra scoperta la cosa s'uccise. Diana dunque lo seguito' in Italia
et Hippolito à sua gloria edifico un Tempio et una chica come si e' detto piu oltre.

III · GUGLIELMO DELLA PORTA · Banquet of the Gods   The Metropolitan Museum of Art

113 · JACOPO BASSANO · Head of a Bearded Man

Janos Scholz

114 · JACOPO TINTORETTO · Head of Vitellius   The Pierpont Morgan Library

The Pierpont Morgan Library

115 · JACOPO TINTORETTO · Man Climbing into a Boat

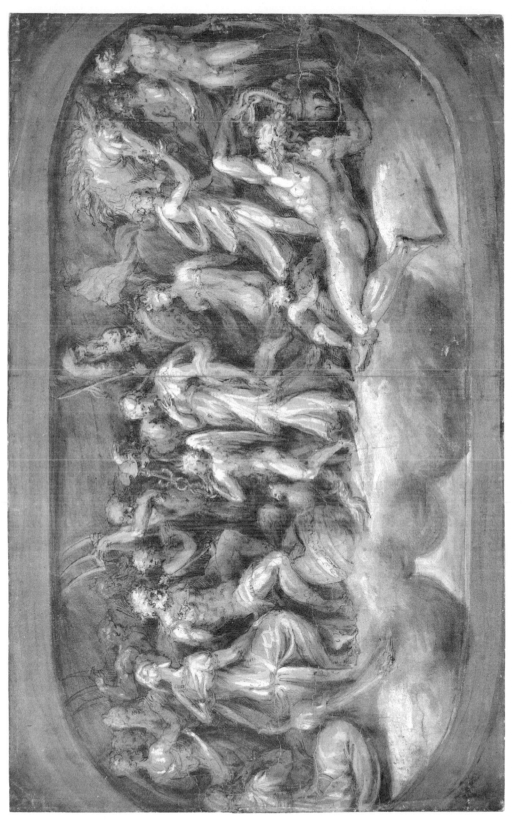

117 · PAOLO FARINATO · Verona
The Pierpont Morgan Library

118 · PAOLO FARINATO · Saints Adoring the Virgin and Child
The Pierpont Morgan Library

120 · LUCA CAMBIASO · St. Sebastian   Robert and Bertina Suida Manning

121 · PELLEGRINO TIBALDI · Seated Figure

The Pierpont Morgan Library

123 · MUZIANO · Arrest of Christ   Janos Scholz

124 · MUZIANO · Seated Male Figure   Janos Scholz

125 · PAOLO VERONESE · Christ Preaching in the Temple
S. Schwarz Collection

126 · PAOLO VERONESE · Studies for a Finding of Moses
The Pierpont Morgan Library

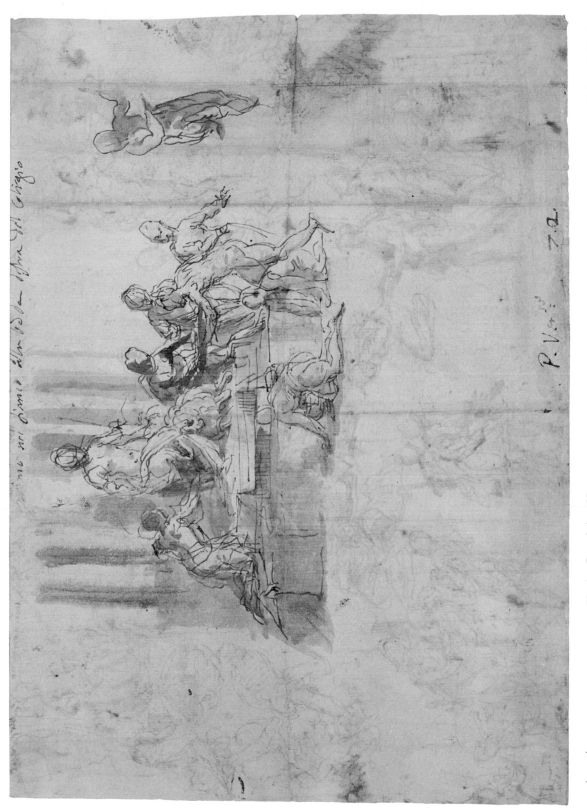

128 · PAOLO VERONESE · Studies for an Assumption of the Virgin and for an Adoration
Robert Lehman

129 · PAOLO VERONESE · Allegory of the Redemption of the World
The Metropolitan Museum of Art

130 · PAOLO VERONESE · Madonna and Child with St. Anne and Angels

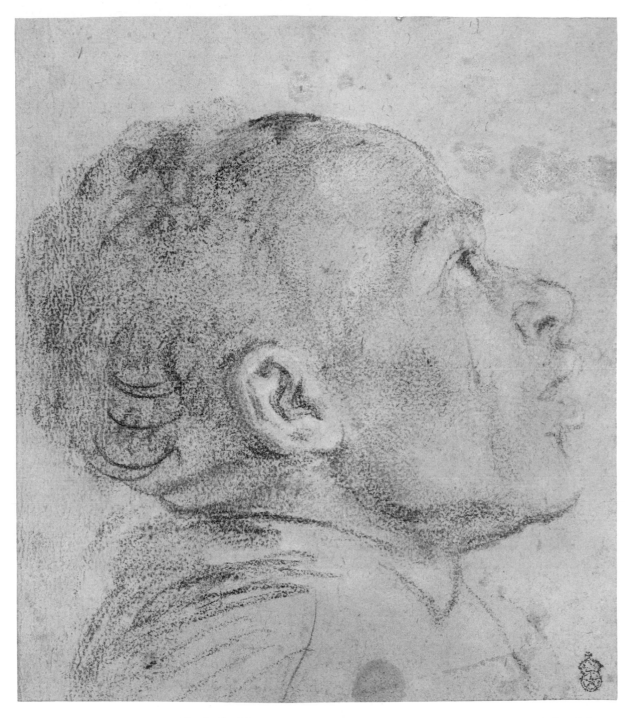

131 · PAOLO VERONESE · Head of a Negro   Robert Lehman

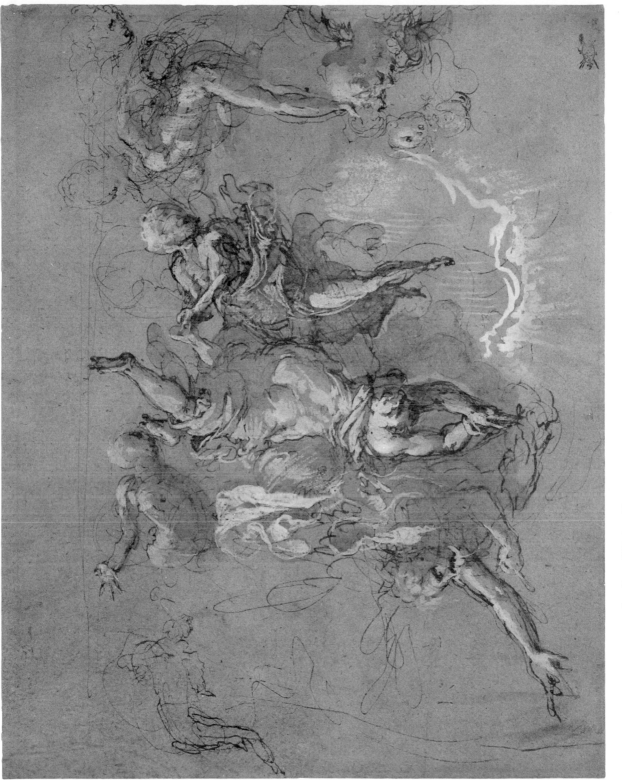

133 · TADDEO ZUCCARO · Studies of Flying Figures

134 · TADDEO ZUCCARO · Studies of Nymphs Bathing   The Metropolitan Museum of Art

134 (verso) · TADDEO ZUCCARO · Studies of Nymphs Bathing   The Metropolitan Museum of Art

135 · TADDEO ZUCCARO · Martyrdom of St. Paul   Robert Lehman

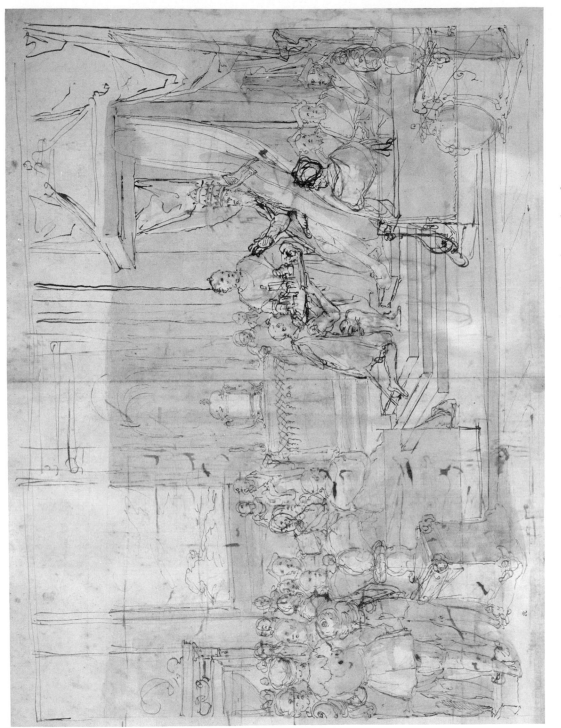

136 · TADDEO ZUCCARO · Pope Julius III Confirming Ottavio Farnese's Title to the Duchy of Parma

138 · GIOVANNI DE' VECCHI · St. John the Evangelist
The Metropolitan Museum of Art

139 · BATTISTA NALDINI · Dead Christ Supported by Three Figures
Walter C. Baker

140 · FEDERICO ZUCCARO · Vision of St. Eustace
The Metropolitan Museum of Art

143 · TROMETTA · St. Matthew

144 · JACOPO BERTOIA · Music-Making Figures anc L⊃▾ers

James J. Rorimer

la morte è fin d'una prigion' oscura

si mosse e disse alie donna che sae

nel mezo del camin di nostra vita

Dopo l'impresa perigliose d'nam

e di sua vita il termine non sae

146 · LIGOZZI · Allegory of Death

147 · POCCETTI · Filippo Benizzi Admonishing Two Women

148 · AMBROGIO FIGINO · Head of a Bearded Man
The Pierpont Morgan Library

149 · LAVINIA FONTANA · Self-Portrait
The Pierpont Morgan Library

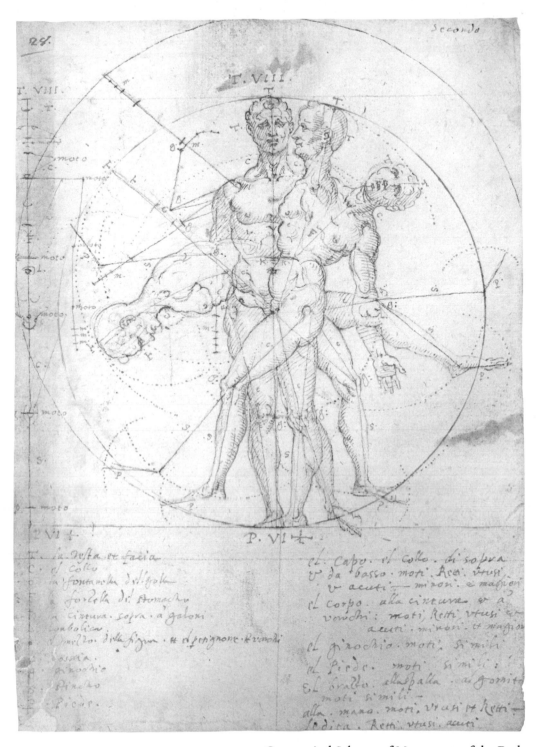

150 · ANONYMOUS MILANESE ARTIST · Geometrical Scheme of Movements of the Body
The Pierpont Morgan Library

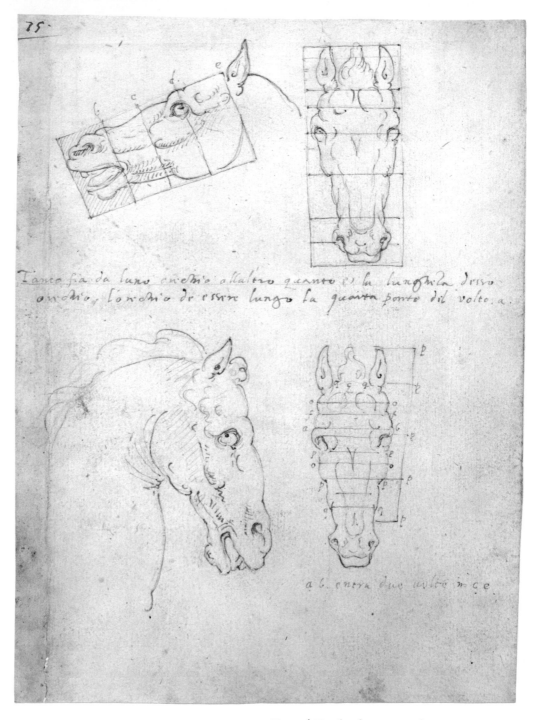

150 A · ANONYMOUS MILANESE ARTIST · Horses' Heads after Leonardo
The Pierpont Morgan Library

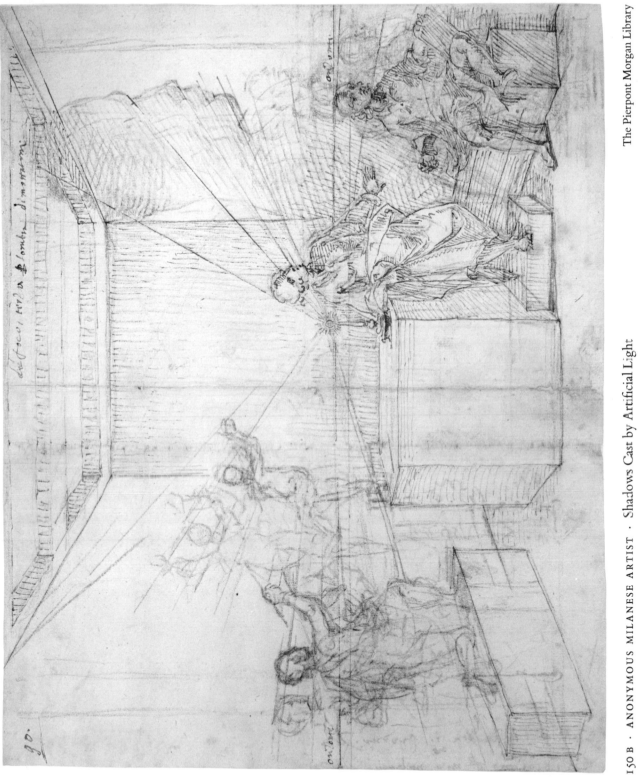

Index of Artists

Designed by Peter Oldenburg. Text composed and printed in English Monotype Bembo by Clarke & Way, Inc., illustrations printed by The Meriden Gravure Company, on Mohawk Superfine Text. Binding by J. F. Tapley Co. First printing, 1965, 7,000 copies.